YOUR LIFE AF

Paddy O'Brien was born in 1953 in Gateshead. She now lives in Southampton and works in personnel consultancy, specialising in management and group work, and work on stress. She has practised and taught yoga for many years. For the past few years she has run active birth classes and seminars at local maternity hospitals. She has four children.

By the same author:

Birth and Our Bodies (Pandora, 1986)

YOUR LIFE AFTER BIRTH

EXERCISES AND MEDITATIONS
FOR THE FIRST YEAR OF
MOTHERHOOD

PADDY O'BRIEN

PANDORA

London   Sydney   Boston

First published by Pandora Press, an imprint of the Trade Division of
Unwin Hyman, in 1988.

PANDORA PRESS
Unwin Hyman Limited
15/17 Broadwick Street, London W1V 1FP

Unwin Hyman Inc
8 Winchester Place, Winchester, MA 01890

Allen & Unwin Australia Pty Ltd
P.O. Box 764, 8 Napier Street, North Sydney, NSW 2060

Allen & Unwin NZ Ltd (in association with the Port Nicholson Press)
60 Cambridge Terrace, Wellington, New Zealand

British Library Cataloguing in Publication Data

O'Brien, Paddy, *1953–*
    Your life after birth: exercises and
    meditations for the first year of
    motherhood.
1. Motherhood. Personal adjustment
I. Title
306.8'743
ISBN 0–86358–266–4

Set in 11 on 13 point Sabon by
Computape (Pickering) Ltd, Pickering, North Yorkshire
and printed in Great Britain by Cox and Wyman Ltd, Reading, Berkshire

Contents

To Z. R. O'B,
With my love.

Acknowledgements

I would like to thank the women who have shared so much and worked so hard at 'Life After Birth' groups. I'd like to thank Sarah Roch and many other members of the Association of Radical Midwives in Hampshire for their support, and Susan Hartley for always being ready to discuss new ideas. Women at Southampton's Women's Education Centre gave me much inspiration in their practice of assertiveness. Many thanks to my editor, Candida Lacey, who has been very supportive. Thanks to Gail Murrey for the speedy typing. Lastly, thanks to Tim, Jon, Ben, Dan and Zoë, for their love and support.

Introduction: what's in the book, how you might use it

When we are pregnant we know that we face labour and birth. It is not so obvious that we also face fifteen or twenty years of living with the child as he or she grows up. Of these, the first year is often the most shocking, the most confusing, the most exhausting. This book is intended as a companion and a guide through that first year. In it you will find nothing about feeding schedules and bedtimes, nor about dummies or the texture of mashed bananas. Instead, this is a record and a sharing of the issues we have found most important in our 'Life After Birth' groups in Southampton and the ways in which we tried to explore them.

During a pregnancy, especially the first one, it is relatively easy to get time and attention for yourself. People often show care and tenderness – even in these angry and difficult times, touched that you are carrying a new life. It is upsetting to find that hardly anyone shows care and tenderness to an exhausted mother struggling with a young baby.

We called our group 'Life After Birth' after the bitter piece of Belfast graffiti – 'Is there life after birth?'. All of us love our babies and feel delighted and privileged to have them, but all of us were aware of unexpected struggles and conflicts in our new lives. Even with second, third, and fourth babies, there were still shocks and surprises.

Each baby is a new personality, and has its place to find in the family or household, affecting you, your partner, your friends and all the other children. Although you have more experience with second and subsequent babies, you have to be more adept and ingenious at juggling time, money and your own physical and emotional energies. How is there ever to be any time for you? In our group we took an hour and a half a week for ourselves and looked at the questions which occupied us most.

The predicament which we are in is this: you get through the pregnancy, you get through the labour, the burning pain as the baby's head comes through, the slither of the little body. You hold your breath waiting for the first plaintive wail. When it comes you laugh or cry or both and lift your baby, and she blinks her newborn eyes open and looks at you. With that look you know, you just know, that whatever else happens, as long as you live, you will never not care what happens to this person. Even when she is taller than you and arguing about her bedtime/hairstyle/motorbike/future she can still throw you a look and you feel that same tug down to the centre of your being. The power of that surge of feeling is shocking and disorientating and needs some good attention.

To many of us as well a wave of unparalleled joy swept over us at the time of our babies' births. We felt as though all the problems of the universe were solved, as though all our lives we had, without knowing it, been waiting for this moment. I looked at each of my children seconds after they were born and felt I could never be unhappy, or anxious, or worried about anything again. No-one would want to miss this intense joy, but it is confusing to find that after a number of days or weeks the euphoria drifts away and the joy is mixed with the complications and miseries of daily existence.

Those are the 'internal' problems. Externally you have to cope in a society which does not call the work you are doing 'work'. 'Oh no, I don't work' is something I regularly hear women say when they are looking after one, two or even more children under school age. The laundry, the catering,

No baby cares about your dream cycle

the nursing, the psychology, the indoor and outdoor play, and the love and understanding they provide is not counted as work at all. The only pay offered for it is about £1.00 a day (child benefit). What about danger money? Quite a lot of the things small babies do are recognised methods of deeply disturbing someone. Systematic interruption of sleep threatens your sanity by disrupting your dream cycles. No baby cares about your dream cycle! He just yells when he wants!

So, you find yourself fatigued and exhausted, even though you are not doing anything that is called 'work'. You are not paid in money for the work. Although it can seem an irritating affectation, some women find it useful to get into the habit of saying 'I don't work *outside the home*' because at least that shows *you* acknowledge your own work in the home.

Furthermore, there is nowhere to bottle or breastfeed a baby comfortably in most shopping areas, it is complicated to have a cup of coffee anywhere with babies and toddlers around, it is murder trying to collapse a double pushchair single-handed and get onto a bus with a toddler and a baby-in-arms, while the rest of the queue gaze at you in stupid disinterest. You can tell it as a funny story afterwards, but at the time your palms sweat, your eyes fill with tears, and panic rises in your throat. Quite reasonably too – it is horrible trying to manage with children in an essentially child-hostile environment.

If you want any time for yourself, or you have to or want to work (*outside* the home), you must find a good carer for your child or children. If you have friends or family nearby they may help, but careful organisation is needed so that you do not get your relations feeling imposed on, or you feeling they have taken your baby or babies over. We are still waiting for creches in the workplace to become any more than a daydream. Baby minders and nannies can be excellent if you can afford them, but still need careful selection. They are expensive and their fees are not tax-deductable (although this is frequently suggested). Many days I go to collect my small children from their baby minder at 3 o'clock – about the time when overfed business men are coming out of the wine bars after their tax-deductable lunches. I watch them with poison in my heart.

If you do work outside the home, everyone will have something to say about it and you need all your emotional resilience to hear both criticism, and support which assumes you have gone back for ideological reasons which you may not share at all. If your pre-baby job was interesting, you may find yourself under fire for choosing to work in the home for a few years.

Nothing will ever be simple again, you think. Exciting, moving, tedious, frightening, wonderful, despairing, and all sorts of other feelings; but never simple. You are probably right.

Babies will get restless

You can use the book in various ways. You can read straight through it, or dip into it, for interest and reference, to see what thoughts it arouses and what ideas it gives you. If you want to work your way through it as a course, it is explained both for a woman working on her own, and for a small group of women working together. Try a chapter about once a week. You need several days for the thoughts you come across to settle in your mind, or rather to spread their ripples; therefore it is better not to rush.

You might want to go through the whole cycle several times. After all, one's feelings close to birth with a milky baby in one's arms are quite different from the way one feels caring for a crawling or toddling vociferous 10- or 11-month-old. However, I would suggest not doing working right through the exercises more often than once every three months. Strong feelings may arise (not necessarily, but they may) and should be given plenty of time to seep through your mental and emotional life.

You do not need much equipment – paper, pens, coloured pens or crayons, comfortable clothes, a bit of peace. The last of these of course is the most elusive. We worked with our babies with us while they were under 6 months of age. If any of the babies was particularly restless we took turns in soothing her. Once they reached about 6 months we found the babies' desire to socialise and their increasing mobility were too distracting, and for ongoing groups decided to meet in the evenings, pooling our resources for a babysitter when that was necessary.

Some ground rules for a group are necessary. The first is the confidentiality of the groups: everyone must commit themselves from the outset to being responsible for keeping the confidence of everybody else. It only needs a moment's thought to see how much harm could be done by anyone speaking of someone else's private thoughts and feelings; and even if no 'actual' harm were done in terms of complicating her relationships, the feeling of trust would be irretrievably gone.

The second rule that may be useful is for each woman to work at her own level. Some women may want and need to be revelatory, and others may feel they like to be more contained and private. Both approaches are workable and valid. Overemphasising the value of revelation, tears, and unleashed emotion can be a mistake. Containment is important too. It seems to me that the biggest issue for women is to have a proper choice. It might be just as pressurising in your group to feel you have to break down as it is at work to feel you must never break down. I do not want to deny the power and importance of tears. I simply mean that neither tears, or any other sort of reaction ought to feel 'compulsory'.

It is useful to agree that your group will meet for a certain number of sessions, to agree on a time limit for each session and to stick to it, avoiding nattering about this and that but staying with the work you've decided to do. It might be useful to make a drink of tea or coffee at the beginning and then not interrupt the flow to make drinks any more during the session. (Although, on reflection, our introductory coffees were always left cold and undrunk at the end of the group.)

Make an agreement at the beginning about smoking or non-smoking and stick to it: with tiny babies around it is of course preferable not to smoke at all, and with valuable women around it is better not to smoke too! If you are a smoker in a non-smoking group you will find it useful to notice what subjects or key words make you want to lurch for a cigarette. Alcohol, cannabis and tranquillisers change your mood by altering your brain chemistry. Do not use them during your sessions. Your ideas will be out of focus and confusing.

We were surprised how much we could find out and how many issues that felt very stuck at the beginning of the sessions loosened up a great deal as we went along. We did not gain much feeling that we could change the world, and were often saddened by that, but we did have a growing feeling that we could change ourselves.

CHAPTER 1

Ourselves – remembering who we are

'Who? You may well ask who.'

This seemed to us to be a good place to begin. Did you know who you were anyway? Womanhood may not have seemed particularly easy to live with even before your baby was a twinkle in your eye, a longing in your heart, a rise on your temperature chart, a diaphragm-less, condom-less moment of passion, or whatever were the particular circumstances before conception. Maybe you could not clearly say 'I'm an archaeologist', 'I'm a woman working at home', 'I'm a business woman, a cleaner, a teacher, a word processor operator, a sportswoman, a saleswoman'. Maybe you were not sure how you saw your future, what your hopes and ambitions were; maybe you were not too sure of your own personal taste and style in music, in clothes, maybe you were not too clear about your feelings about the powerful relationships in your lives – with friends, parents, partners. Maybe your life has felt like one long struggle to survive, or one long muddle. On the other hand perhaps you had a clear lifestyle and a strong sense of personal and/or professional identity.

Either way, pregnancy and birth throw a large spanner in the works. The foetus inside may seem to be an invader, an intruder, a beloved baby, a friend, making you sick, hot, and heavy, battering you with his tiny hands and fists, heaving his knees and elbows in movements visible through your abdomen and sometimes through your clothes as well. He hiccups, and bounces on your bladder causing you to need to pee every thirty-five minutes day and night. You put your hand on your tummy and he swims over and pushes into it. You feel tenderness, resentment, anger and love. So much energy, physical and emotional, goes into the shared life, shared body, of pregnancy.

And then the baby bursts out through the softest, most secret, most intimate part of you, leaving you empty, and sometimes bruised and torn. Your breasts fill with milk – for days they ache and leak. You try to get into a rhythm of feeding, crying, sleeping. The flowers and champagne, if they happen at all, last precisely ten days. The midwife makes her last visit, your partner goes back to work, the front door closes behind them both. There you are. The two of you. Getting on with it. No wonder, no wonder at all you feel confused, vulnerable, strange.

It sounds as though I am trying to say that having a baby is nothing but misery. I do not mean to say that. The flood of love, the intimate and poignant time with a young baby seems to me to be one of the most beautiful experiences life has to offer. The tiny flower-like body moving softly, the wide newborn-blue eyes gazing at you, the smell of the baby that you inhale deeply as you lay your cheek on her downy fragile head, are intoxicating. The smiles and cooing noises that come a few weeks later are literally thrilling; when you see and hear them they send thrills through you like electric shocks. Personally, I would not have missed any of that for worlds. However, it is *also* true that one is lonely, vulnerable, frightened, broke, and tired. It is revolting that we are sold a roseate picture of motherhood by stores and magazines who want our money for designer props and costumes for the fantasy – but do not have enough true information about the difficult and painful side.

The first piece of work we decided to do to begin to surface from the haze of broken nights and churned-up emotions was this: to ask ourselves what kind of person am I? What am I like? What do I enjoy? Hate? Love? Fear? What am I clear about? Where am I enigmatic or puzzled? We did not attempt a full and conclusive definition, we attempted an exploration, a remembering, a classifying. We attempted, for an hour and a half, to put ourselves first, to concentrate on ourselves. Choose five or six of the exercises below to work on 'yourself'. Choose a mixture of thinking, talking, writing, drawing, and physical exercises. If you are working by yourself, have a notebook, and write down the things you would have said in a group. You do not have other people's feedback, but you do have a record of your reactions which you can read over and reflect on, and you do have a book that you can share with someone else in the future if you choose to.

The first group of exercises is useful for starting a session, or for use towards the beginning of a session; those in the second section are useful for the middle part; those in the third section are useful towards the end of, or to close, a session.

Section one – starting off and warming up

Exercise 1   Name game 1

Go around the group introducing yourself by saying your name and one positive quality about yourself, beginning with the same letter (or sound) as your name. This exercise serves a number of purposes. Everyone's voice is quickly heard – this helps to stop anyone who feels very shy becoming stuck in a silence. It is quite silly and quite difficult and immediately has people laughing and helping each other. Also you have immediately set the precedent of presenting yourself in a positive light. Daft though it may feel in some ways, it makes you feel quite different presenting yourself as 'Powerful Paddy' rather than 'Pathetic Paddy' for instance. When you have done your round of 'Gorgeous Gail', 'Sumptuous Susan', 'Able Ann', 'Loving Lucy', 'Sensitive Surinder', 'Mus al Maggie' and so forth, you will also find that you ca remember each other's names pretty well – the extra associative word has fixed them clearly.

Exercise 2   Name game 2

An alternative name game that is also fun and makes the names memorable is one where you invent a (likely or unlikely) mode of transport beginning with the same letter as your name: 'I'm Kathy and I came on a kite', 'I'm Bea and I came by balloon', 'I'm Tessa and I came on a tractor', 'I'm Julie and I came by jet'. It produces a pleasant cartoon-like image of everyone speeding to the group on their more or less surreal transport. 'I'm Sally,' said one particularly warm, loving and peaceful woman, 'and I came

Name game 2

Name game 2

by subterranean nuclear missile.' This image startled us and her as well, but as the weeks went by the metaphorical truth of what had popped spontaneously into her mind emerged. She used her time in the group to explore some of her darker side and her darker feelings about motherhood, which co-exist with her loving side, sometimes uneasily.

My own first response to this exercise was 'I'm Paddy and I came by parachute' – this too had its resonance about landing somewhere unknown and dangerous, 'behind the lines', and being vulnerable and having to improvise . . . so even in an apparently trivial exercise there can be some riches.

When I was doing some work in the Southampton Civic Centre a woman approached me in a corridor and said 'Hello – I'm looking for health'. My heart went out to her! – and I longed to respond 'Yes – so am I!' Of course she meant she was looking for the Department of Environmental Health – but the poetry of her sentence stayed with me for many days.

Exercise 3   What do you want?

How many times have frustrated partners, parents, doctors, friends, said to you, 'What is it that you *want*?' when confronted with your confusion or your distress. In this 'What on earth do you want?' question, there are of course underlying messages – surely you already have everything you want, why do you have to be so awkward and complicated, what is the *matter* with you?

Supposing we start from an assumption that there is nothing wrong with you, that you have come to a group or are working on these exercises on your own because you are interested in getting clearer about things. Give each person three or four minutes to speak about what she wants from the sessions; or if you are writing in a book, take two or three pages to write down what you want from your explorations. Suppose nobody says 'Don't be silly' or 'I don't think you'll get *that*' or, if you are working alone, suppose you do not criticise yourself for what you want and need – just let your wishes be, and let them be heard. You may be surprised to hear them yourself – safe from the fear of censure you may be surprised to hear what's going on inside you.

Exercise 4   What do you bring?

Most women can hold forth about their weaknesses eloquently for lengthy speeches. Maybe we practise doing it a lot and that's why we are so good at it. Do not do that – try instead for each person to say three good qualities that they bring to the group. Although your palms sweat and your throat goes dry try to say very definitely what the qualities are. Try not to say 'I'm quite a good listener sometimes, I suppose'. Try out 'I'm a very good listener' – and then *breathe* – you may be amazed how much one is tempted to hold one's breath after saying something that makes one tense. Sometimes you can't quite think of three positive qualities. Sharon said 'I bring the group my commitment' – (deep sighing breath) – 'I bring my honesty' – (trembling breath, pause) – 'and I bring my cold!' Well, fair enough. (We did not catch her cold, but did benefit from her commitment and honesty right through the weeks.) Working alone, take some time to write your strengths and good qualities down. However, do not just write them down in cold biro like a shopping list. Get your coloured pens and make pictures of the words, as large as you like, and decorate the words with colours and patterns that illustrate and celebrate the strong qualities you have recognised in yourself.

Sometimes someone in a group will become very upset because she cannot think of anything good that she has got to bring with her. She needs time, and support if she wants it. Check, either with a questioning look, or in words, whether it would be helpful for someone to hold her hand or put their arms around her while she stays with her feelings. Although one's instinct is to rush in and 'make it alright' by saying what you think is good about her if she's someone you know, or generally making reassuring noises (if she's someone you do not know) that is not very respectful of her feelings. If she feels so useless it is because of important things that have happened to her and have been said to her and that should not be brushed aside. It would be more helpful to prompt her by asking 'When did you last feel strong? What were you doing? Can you bring any of that strength here?' or 'When did you last feel proud?' or 'When were you last gentle with someone? Can you bring that gentleness here?' But be sparing with such questions and do not 'pester' her with them. Sometimes, after a pause and with a little support, she will be able to find and recognise a strength. Extend your waiting silence while it feels good and while it does not feel pressurising to the person concerned, or restless to everyone else. If, after that, she really does not want to say anything or feel she can, leave it. The fact that everyone made space for her feelings of uselessness and did not criticise her for them is the important thing.

If you are working alone and feel you have nothing good to write down about yourself, do not panic. Try a similar method of asking yourself when you last felt brave, or tough, or gentle, or patient. When were you last resourceful or imaginative? When did you last show endurance and courage? When did you last do something skilful or make something well? A positive answer to any of those questions will give you one positive quality to start from. If you still feel entirely useless, give yourself a little time to notice gently that events and people in your life must have piled up onto you to make you feel so useless. If you feel sad make a picture of the word 'sad', in the way I have suggested making pictures of the positive words, and decorate it with colours and patterns that tell of your sadness. If you need to cry while doing so, carry on. Tears are often a sign of strength rather than weakness, and maybe women have a lot of tears because they are doing so many other people's crying for them, as well as their own.

One last point on this exercise: it seems unlikely that any woman goes through childbirth and looking after a small baby without having heroic courage, great patience and love, and tremendous endurance. It might be good for one's own self-esteem to notice that properly. It might be good for informing the rest of the world to SHOUT IT VERY LOUDLY INDEED.

Section two – the middle part of the session

Exercise 5   People find it easy to see/people find it difficult to see

Take a piece of paper or a fresh page in your notebook and divide it into two columns, headed as above – on the left, 'people find it easy to see', and on the right, 'people find it difficult to see'. Then have a good five minutes to write in the two columns. On the 'easy to see' side, for instance, you might want to put 'how efficient I am', whereas on the 'difficult to see' side, you might want to put 'how frightened I am'. Maybe it's easy to see how fit you are, but difficult to see how much you worry about your weight. Perhaps it's easy to see how dynamic you are but hard to see how much strain your marriage is putting on you; easy to see how bad you are at housework, hard to see how hard you try to keep the squalor down. You do not have to set things down in pairs – you can put a whole string of 'easy' points without matching 'difficult' points, and vice versa. Write down whatever comes into your head however trivial it seems, because the very fact that it came into your head means that it has something to tell you. After five minutes go round the circle sharing the material that is on your lists and what you feel about it. Notice what kind of things are on the 'easy' side, and what kind of things on the 'difficult'. Of the 'easy' side – why are those things the things which people notice? Do you present or display them? Are you pleased about them? Or angry, or humiliated, or a mixture? Look at your feelings about each point on the list. Then consider the 'difficult' list. Consider whether people find these things difficult to see because you choose to hide them – and if you do, why, and whether you are glad to keep them private or would prefer to show and share them more – or whether people find them difficult to see because they prefer not to notice them. See if any pattern emerges.

Working alone, consider your own lists fully, and just listen to anything they have to tell you, and any surprises they have. Do you show your feelings but cover up your physical and practical difficulties? Do you show your weaknesses and hide your strengths? Or the other way around? Do you feel the people around you are blind to certain things about you? Or do you wish they did not see you quite so acutely? Is there anything that stands out as something you would like to change? If so, at this stage, just notice it and bear it in mind. You cannot make radical changes in attitude or behaviour through an act of will, but you can sow a seed in your mind of a desire for change and it will usually grow in strength just by you giving it some space.

Exercise 6   Hand massage

In pairs, sit comfortably opposite one another. One person should take one of her partner's hands gently onto her lap and give it a massage. Begin with her palm upwards, support it in your left hand, and with your right thumb begin in the centre of the palm and with slow movements stroke and loosen it. Then lightly stroke and pull along the thumb and each finger, giving a gentle pull at each joint. When you feel the hand is warm and relaxed, gently turn it over and stroke slowly several times along the back of the hand and fingers. When you finish give the hand gently back, and shake your own hands, in recognition that you shake off any charge or tension you absorbed from your partner's hand. While you work be as receptive as you can, see what you can perceive through your hands. Meanwhile, the person being massaged should talk about her own hands. She should tell the story of her hands. What do they look like? What do they feel like? What are they good at? What do they enjoy? What do they do? Mention any injury or accident that has happened to your hands. Say anything else that comes into your head about your hands. Also let the person doing the massage say anything that she notices about your hands.

Hands are touching — in both senses of the word. They are expressive and particularly human, and unique from person to person. One of the most loving things we can do is hold hands. Our hands do so much work, give so much pleasure. We can release a lot of emotion, find out things about ourselves, by giving and receiving attention about our hands. British medical students often begin their training by dissecting a human corpse. When new students come into the lab to do this it is often the cadaver's hands which are bound up to spare the students' feelings — rather than the faces or anything else. It is the hands which are so indicative that this was once a living, feeling and moving person, and which must be covered until the students are accustomed to the work.

Although the lessons of anatomy learned through dissection are obviously vitally important, one wonders how much chance medical students get to deal with their feelings about death, or about beginning their study of the healing art with a dead body, in any other way than being very hearty about it. One doctor told me that the first instruction she read on her first day as she stood next to her cadaver was this: 'Saw off the top of the skull. If the brains are liquid, pour them out. If they are solid, scoop them out.' (This doctor eventually specialised in psychiatry!)

To return to our living hands — use this exercise as another way of talking about yourself. Notice whether you feel your hands are strong, or sensitive, or artistic, or rough — battered or injured, painted and creamed, dirty and scuffed — burned anywhere, cut anywhere, stained with paint or nicotine or dye. Are they practical hands, sensual hands, or both, or neither? What machinery can they work, what boats can they sail, what cars can they drive? Do they paint, draw, make love, soothe children? And so on, and so on, and so on. Angela's hands were baby smooth and plump on the outside (the backs of her hands), finely but densely lined all over on the inner palms and fingers. On reflection this gave her a lot of ideas to work on, about hidden experience and a smooth exterior, and about a hidden desire to paint and draw enclosed in a persona quite different from that of an artist. Do not strive to interpret in this or any exercise – say what you want to say, try to hear it clearly, and then say whatever else arises in your mind because of it.

On your own: when I was at junior school we had an unpleasant joke about how staring at your own hands was the first sign of madness. Thus, attempting this exercise on my own would have rather odd connotations for me! However, if that joke was not part of your 9–year-old folk lore, you may be able to work through this alone. You can give yourself a hand massage, though it lacks the warmth of another person's attention. You might like instead to try the set of yoga hand and finger stretches put into a charming narrative sequence on pages 62–3 of Ros Widdowson's elegant, if optimistically titled book *Yoga Made Easy*. You can also describe your own hands carefully, write your descriptions and observations down, and simply take notice of any surprises or connections, depressing or encouraging associations you come across.

Exercise 7   *Favourite clothes*

Get into pairs. If you also picked the last exercise, change round this time and work with someone else. Have three or four minutes (timed) each and tell your partner about your favourite article of clothing (or footwear, a hat, or jewell-ery). Describe it clearly and explain what you like about it and what you feel it expresses about you. It might be an old and beloved pullover that has been everywhere with you, or something new and special bought as a celebration or a treat of some kind. Take time to explain why this particular pair of earrings or T-shirt or pair of boots means a lot to you. If you have nothing at all that you like at the moment use some of your time to describe why – are you too broke, do you feel too fat, or too guilty, or too confused? Any or all of these would be important factors in your life, and should be noted and talked about. If you have a feeling of something you would like if only you could afford it, or felt able to buy it, then speak about that and why you would like it, and what you feel it would do for you.

The way we present ourselves visually is an endlessly fascinating subject. By the way we dress we express in a finely adjusted way who we think we are, what we think we are worth, exactly what our allegiances are socially, poli-tically and within the different groups we operate in: 'She's the sort of woman who wears a navy suit and carries a white handbag'; 'Of course, she's always wearing dun-garees'. Both give you an instant picture of a person and her probable attitudes. We locate ourselves somewhere within the sexual struggle, choosing cuts, colours and textures expressing the feminist or the feminine, or attempting a compromise. We dress to mask or emphasise our curves, our height; we dress to look unusual, or we dress to blend in. We may opt out of the whole thing, covering ourselves with serviceable clothes, using and using them till they wear out, or may invest a large amount of time and money in obtaining and maintaining particular items, and selecting each day what to wear. It all tells you something about yourself.

Further points worth thinking and talking about in this

area are these: how did/do your parents like you to dress? How about your partners – do they prefer you to dress in any particular way? Have you ever worn a uniform, at school or at work? How have different uniforms felt to you? Do your children prefer you to dress in any particular way? Include these in your discussion if you find them interesting. If you are working on your own, write about your favourite piece of clothing, giving yourself time to reflect on why you are fond of it and how it expresses something about you. If it interests you, write also about what other important people in your life have wanted you to wear, and about any uniforms you have worn and how you have felt wearing them.

Exercise 8   Drawing

Felt-tip pens or coloured wax crayons give quick vivid colours for drawing. At first most people howl with dismay 'but I can't draw – I never could'. In fact we all could when we were small children and what most of us suffer from is a growing inhibition and a growing doubt and eventually we decide that we can't. If you forget about anything looking realistic or 'correct' and just make pictures of what you wish, you will probably find that you *can* draw.

First of all, take five minutes to draw a tree. Use the colours you please, and do it however you like. When you stop drawing, if you are in a group, glance around you and you will see a great variety of different trees. Look again at your own tree and notice points such as these: are the lines heavy, continuous, light or hesitant? Are there leaves, flowers or fruit? Is there life or activity in the tree, or around it? Have you put in a background? If so, what is it like? Where on the paper have you put it – filling the whole page, or tiny, up in one corner, or spilling off the top of the paper, or pushing off the lower edge of the page? What sort of shape is the tree? What sort of mood does it seem to be in or suggest? Then talk to the group about the tree you have drawn. Don't try to 'interpret' it, but talk about it and see what emerges.

We saw trees against night skies, with stars and a crescent moon behind and an owl and nest crouching in the branches. We saw trees laden with snow, or heavy with round red apples. One woman drew a spreading tree against rolling hills with the sun setting behind them, and a path flowing from the tree over the hills to the sun. Another drew a tree with swings and birdhouses fixed in it, and said how cross she felt that she always saw everything in terms of providing opportunities for others. Some trees look positively jovial while others look like rockets or explosions. Broken branches may speak of traumas or separations, and groups of anything may relate to configurations or groups in your own life. Sarah drew three small flowers at the foot of her tree and one more flower a little way off. Looking at them she said – oh yes, these are my brothers and sisters – and the one by itself is my sister who died.

As with all the other exercises the point is not to explain your tree, to analyse it, and to come to conclusions about it, but to look at something drawn fairly spontaneously and notice anything that has made itself available to you in your picture. Strangely enough, this still works even if you 'know' you are going to think about what you have drawn afterwards, so long as you let yourself draw what you really want to draw at that particular moment. (Occasionally a 'test' like this will be used as part of an interview or selection procedure, and one can hardly blame people who feel unfairly pried into by this for 'faking' them – by putting in deep roots, fruits and a very balanced and productive tree generally. Some of the early astronauts record having faked their Rorschach tests – where one is asked to 'see pictures' in a random ink blot – in order to come over as normal, balanced and healthy.)

You might like to take two more pieces of paper and make two more drawings. On your first piece of paper take five minutes to make a picture of your relationships with women. Use the next five minutes and your next piece of paper to make a picture of your relationships with men. Then go around the group and have four or five minutes each to speak about your pictures. Again, the first thing one notices is the richness and variety of imagination, seeing how some women choose to express themselves in diagrams, some in cartoons, some in abstract patterns, and some in realistic or stylised drawings. Making these pictures can give you useful insights into how you feel about getting on with women and men. The major characters in your life and past will appear in your drawing or patterns. Notice what kind of differences there are in the two pictures. Look at what you draw, and listen carefully to yourself so that you hear clearly what you are saying.

Exercise 9   Guided fantasy on the Quality of the Self

One person should read this fantasy out, rather slowly, making a pause between each sentence and the next. Everyone else can participate. If you are working alone, read the fantasy through several times until the train of thought is clear to you. Lie yourself down comfortably and let the fantasy slowly drift through your mind.

Take a few deep breaths and sigh them away through your mouth, then let your breathing settle as it wants to – probably it will be slow and light. Let your body feel soft, warm and heavy. Let your head be heavy. Where you are in contact with the floor, let yourself sink into the floor a little more. Let your feet relax, let your hands curl softly like a small child's.

Now take yourself in your imagination to a beautiful garden. Walk into the garden and look all around you. See the lovely garden all around you. Choose your favourite place in the garden and walk steadily to the place. Make yourself comfortable in that place and lay yourself down there for a rest. Be aware of the sights and the sounds all around you. Settle down and relax, soaking up the warmth of the sun. Resting in your garden let your mind travel through your life – your experiences as a younger woman, as a little girl, as a baby. Notice any times in your life where you felt particularly strong, particularly clear, particularly happy. Notice any times where you really felt happy in yourself. Notice any times at all that come to mind, however small the incident, however fleeting the moment. Hold those happy times, those times you really felt you were yourself, for a moment in your mind.

Now ask yourself, is there a word, or an image, or a colour, or any music, that expresses your quality, as you are when you feel really at one with the world, happy, and at peace. If there is a word, or an image, or a colour, or any music, that seems to tell of yourself, as you are when you feel really at one with the world, hold it gently in your mind.

(Pause.)

Now begin to wake yourself up. Begin by taking some deeper breaths and yawning them out. Take a deep breath in again, and yawn it out again. Stretch your fingers, stretch your toes. Stretch your arms and your legs. If you are lying on your back curl up and roll over onto your side, and rest there for a moment or two before pressing your hands into the floor to help yourself to sit up. The guided fantasy is now finished.

After this fantasy people are often very quiet, subdued, and inward-looking. Ask them to find a partner, without disturbing themselves too much, just turning quietly to the person next to them. It is useful simply to hold hands or put a hand on each other's shoulders for a few minutes until you feel ready to talk. When you do feel ready to talk, describe to each other what kind of a garden you saw, what plants and birds and insects you saw and heard. Describe the place you chose to lie down, and then share, from your scanning of your life, the times when you felt fulfilled and really yourself. Share too the image, or words, colours or music, that you feel represent you when you are most yourself. Then listen to your partner while she shares her fantasy with you.

This fantasy is a way of contacting what you feel the core qualities – the central qualities – of yourself might be. It is very moving and often releases tears, it can be dreadfully upsetting if a woman has a sense of it being years and years since she was 'really herself', or exhilarating if a woman feels she is just 'coming into herself'. If you thought your way through the fantasy on your own, wake up very slowly and rest, lying down, as long as you like. When you finally feel like sitting up, write in your book about the garden you saw, the place you rested, the times you saw in your life when you felt happy and clear. Write about and draw the words and images that came into your mind, describing the core or essential ones for you at those times.

Section three – exercises for finishing the session

Choose one or more of these exercises to close your session.

Exercise 10   Back massage

In pairs, give one another a back massage. One person sits tall and cross-legged and her partner, sitting or kneeling behind her, can knead and loosen her shoulders, and supporting her hands on the sides of the ribcage, stroke from the spine outwards with her thumbs. Massage her lower back with the heels of your hands. Massage from shoulders down to the sacrum three or four times. Finish with long strokes down the back with the whole hands and then shake your hands out, signifying that you shake off anything you absorbed from your partner. Your partner will probably be very reluctant for you to stop! However, when you have finished, stop and change around.

Exercise 11   Something for you

Think of a small treat you can be sure to give yourself during the week. Go round your group and get each person to share what her treat will be – long relaxing baths, or a couple of hours to read, or to wander pushchairless around the shops while somebody else looks after the baby feature quite prominently among our groups' choices. So do chances to do childlike things oneself (crunching through autumn leaves, stomping in puddles) – including the choice that one woman made at a particular moment in the year, to pop some of the unopened fuschia buds. A new pair of earrings, or a sauna bath, if affordable, are often chosen, or it might be a couple of hours with a good friend, or a long cuddle. Take some time to think carefully of something particular and feasible you would really like, and make sure you make it happen during the week.

Exercise 12   Deep relaxation

Don't choose this way of closing your session if you did the 'guided fantasy' (Exercise 9), it will leave you feeling too remote and too floppy. Otherwise, it can be a lovely way to finish. Find some slow, gentle music if you can and play it quietly. Relax on the floor. In the rhythm of your breathing, tighten and relax each group of muscles in turn. Breathing in tighten your feet, breathing out let them go – let them be heavy and soft. Tighten a little in your legs as you breathe in – as you breathe out, let your legs go – let them go heavy and relaxed. Go right through your body – hips, abdomen, chest, arms and hands, throat, neck, face and head. Finally rest, your whole body heavy and relaxed.

Take yourself in your imagination to somewhere you would really like to be. It could be a warm and sunny beach, or some favourite garden, or somewhere in the countryside, or anywhere where you really feel at home, or at peace. Take yourself there and lie yourself down there for a rest. After some time, you will find yourself surfacing again, becoming aware again of the room around you and the people around you. Wake yourself up slowly – taking some deep breaths, yawning them out, stretching your fingers and toes, your arms and your legs. If you are resting on your back, curl up and roll over onto your side, resting curled up for a few moments. When you feel like sitting up, push your hands into the floor to help yourself up.

Women working alone should do both Exercises 11 and 12; if you are going to spend time alone working hard and thinking hard about difficult and stirring thoughts, you must make sure you have time, in straightforward and gentle ways, to be kind to yourself.

Leave a week now until you do any more work on this, but write in your book any thoughts that come to you in the interval, also any memorable dreams that arise. Women working in a group might like to keep a notebook too, since women often talk about the hours and days immediately following the group as being particularly fertile in ideas and insights. Note them down as and when they arise.

CHAPTER 2

Our Mothers – and ourselves as mothers

When you have a baby you cannot avoid the issue of what motherhood is really all about. Our feelings run high about how we want to bring our own children up, and the way other people treat their own children can annoy, or worry, or challenge us considerably. We have a feeling of what is expected of us as mothers and a sense of which of those expectations we accept and which we want to reject. Of those we accept, we have a feeling of how much we do or do not live up to them. Of those we reject, we may have feelings of anger or guilt about some. In addition to this, our own experience of being mothered becomes vivid. Memories of being a small child come back clearly, and upheavals of emotion occur where no clear memory emerges, but where some disturbance from very long ago is obviously being reactivated.

In some ways our connections with our mothers are renewed. Phrases that your mother used to say pop out of *your* mouth – and you feel 'where on earth did that come from?'. You may feel a sudden understanding of her protective feelings towards you, feelings which, as an adolescent, you rejected because they made you feel stifled. Or, if your family circumstances were different you may feel it the other way round – that you are angry and shocked that your mother did not seem to love and protect you as well as you feel you love and protect your baby. If you were separated from your mother when you were very young, you may feel that separation again, acutely.

There may be a new bond. Jean travelled hundreds of miles only days after her daughter was born, because she felt an urgent desire to talk to her mother about her daughter's birth. She described it as a 'primitive' feeling – a conversation over the telephone with her would not do, she wanted to be *with* her. They felt very close, especially since the patterns of their first labours had been similar. Also, after a long adolescence and early womanhood and of having very little in common with your mother, you may find the baby is a marvellous source of mutual interest and love. If you are in a delicate enough balance with each other you may be able to exchange views and enjoy your mother's ability to give you advice about looking after your baby. (For ideas about dealing with *unwelcome* advice, look at chapter 4 on 'Assertiveness'.) A general sense of shared womanhood may make common ground between you both where none existed before.

Some years ago my maternal grandmother was dying, slowly and painfully. I paid a short visit to her with my mother. It was difficult to talk much. While we tried to find things to say, when the real things were far too hard to say, I had a sudden vision of our three wombs, like three bells, and how precious it was to me that mine was still fertile and likely to live a long time. I had a moment of feeling part of a succession of women. Within the next three years I had two more children not, of course, simply because of that moment, but not unconnected with it either. An impulse towards birth can be part of being in touch with a death, or other kind of loss of a mother or grandmother, which puts us in touch with our own mortality.

The following exercises should help to open up your

thoughts about motherhood, mothering, and being mothered. Choose a selection, but take at least one from each section – a first section exercise, a middle section exercise and a finishing exercise. Try to choose a mixture of physical, talking and writing exercises.

Section one – exercises to begin the session

Exercise 13   *How are you?*

'How are you today?' 'Fine, fine.' 'And how's the baby?' 'Oh, she's lovely, thank you. We're very lucky.' How many times have you had a conversation like that, when if you were going to say what was really going on it would go – 'How are you today?' 'Well, I'm exhausted, my stitches are still sore, one of my nipples is cracked, I feel like crying all the time, and I've got nobody to talk to.' 'And how's the baby?' 'She's feeding every two hours day and night and cries all through the evening from 8 to 11 p.m. so I never get a chance to talk to my partner at all. Her last few nappies were a funny colour and I don't know what to do about it.'

Or it might be – 'How are you today?' 'Well, physically I'm alright but I'm supposed to be going back to work in six weeks' time and I can't find a babyminder and I feel in a total panic about leaving the baby anyway.' 'And how's the baby?' 'He's drinking all his bottles so fast he's vomiting them up, and I think he might need some solids but the health visitor's dead against me starting him on them yet. He's more interesting and lovely every day, and I can't imagine leaving him, but I do miss my work.'

Of course, life would be very complicated if, every time somebody asked you how you were, you actually told them – it is understood that it's normally no more than a ritual. But, now's your chance.

Sit down quietly and take time to think carefully how you are. Write these thoughts down. If you are in a group make use of the other women. Give each woman in the group a few minutes to think about the question 'How are you?'. That few minutes is necessary to get past the reflex 'Fine, thank you' and the blanket 'Bloody awful' to something more specific. Then give everyone a little time to say briefly but precisely exactly how she is. Liz said simply 'I'm happy, because I'm changing'. Gill said 'I'm hot and flustered because I couldn't find my keys for ages before I set off, and I couldn't find anywhere to park when I got here, so I was late again. I feel worried about everything and nothing – my partner can't help me because I can't tell him clearly enough what it is that's bothering me. This is the end of an awful week – lots of small things have gone wrong and I feel as though I've been struggling against the odds all week.' Sue said 'I'm going hot and cold because my period's late. My palms keep going sweaty every time I think about it. I just cannot cope if I'm pregnant again now. I can't concentrate on anything else, it just keeps coming into my mind.' Mary said 'I am well and things are going well with my baby, but I have a growing feeling of really hating men, which is difficult to cope with. I just think about my brothers and the way they use my mother, and I really hate them. My husband is one of those caring men that everybody else thinks is wonderful but I want to say to him "Look here, you're *just about* OK, nothing special, and the rest are just total bastards". So that's how I am, I'm confused and worried about men.' And Diane said 'I'm alright, I'm fine. She [the baby] doesn't cry so much any more, and she's smiling at me and cooing at me; but I have to go back to work in two months' time, and I just don't know how to begin to get back. I'm enjoying being with *her* [the baby] but I don't know how I'm going to get back to work.' Sarah said 'I'm not anything. I don't know how I am. I'm not anything at all. Someone came to the door to do a survey and said "What are you?" or "What do you do?" or something, and I couldn't answer. I couldn't say house-wife, or mother, or historian [her job], or anything. I don't know anything about myself any more. I don't know how I am.'

The opportunity to notice how you are, and to share clearly how you are with other people, can be very useful. Obviously the sharing is supportive, and fun, and gives you a feeling of lessening the isolation and pressure you are under. It is useful to hear clearly that other people's lives are complicated too. The first part, the 'noticing' part, is important too. It is useful practice and a valuable skill to be able to put a hand on how you are in a precise way. If you feel happy, or peaceful, or fulfilled, it is useful to know in what situations and circumstances you feel those things — maybe you can arrange to have more of them! If you feel low, giving it a specific name — demoralised, confused, fatigued or whatever, rather than just miserable or depressed — can begin to identify it clearly, which in turn gives you a chance to do something about it.

Exercise 14   Wake up!

Too much sitting talking can give you a sluggish feeling physically. If your group feels listless or swamped with negative feelings, fit this exercise in to make you laugh and wake you up. Get into pairs. One person should bend over at the waist and flop like a rag doll. She should turn her head from side to side a few times to relax her neck. Her partners should then slap with both hands (alternately, like drumming) all the way down one side of her back and down the back of that leg, then all the way down the other side of her back and down the back of that leg. Start at the top of the shoulder and go right down to the foot. Go all

Slapping exercise

over both sides of her back and both legs again. Now the person being slapped should stand up, while her partner slaps all down her arms, tummy, and legs (avoid breastfeeding breasts at all costs!) and gently over her face. When this is finished swap roles.

You will find this leaves you feeling tingling and invigorated. Perhaps it's also enjoyable to have a chance to hit someone! I don't know about that, but as a way of waking yourself up it is quick and easy and beats the small child's early morning method of sitting on your chest in her soaking nappy and prising your eyes open with her fingers.

On your own this exercise is tricky! However, standing up and having a good shake or a good stretch, or dancing to a favourite piece of music, has a good effect. (Can the neighbours see? – who cares! If you do, draw the curtains. It is a bit inhibiting if the postman comes up the path just when you're giving your all, like Isadora Duncan or Hot

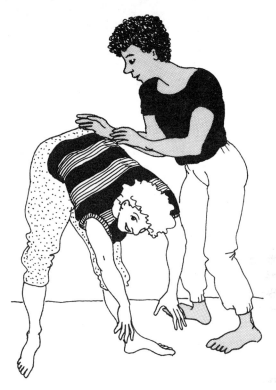

Slapping exercise

Gossip.) In general we probably should stop several times a day for a stretch or physical loosen-up – it is not in-built in our culture so tends not to occur to us. We have all seen videos of workers at the Nissan factory stopping every few hours for their exercises. Visitors to Japan also mention people out carrying heavy loads of shopping or firewood, putting their load down and doing a little *Tai chi* to recover their muscles and their equilibrium. We could probably all do to remember that a few minutes stretching a few times a day can tip our mood and our physical relaxation from a deteriorating to an improving condition.

Exercise 15   Mirroring

Working in a group, choose a partner. Choose who is to be the 'real' person first and who the reflection. Let the real person move around the room, exploring, bending, stretching, twirling, sitting, kneeling, lying, grimacing, jumping, anything you like. The reflection should copy as precisely as she can, mirroring her partner's every move. After a couple of minutes change around and take opposite roles. When you finish take a few minutes to tell each other how it felt. Notice how springy or sluggish your body felt, and whether it was easier to lead or follow.

This exercise, like the previous one, offers a chance to move around the room and loosen up. It releases tension in laughter, and gives an opportunity to touch on feelings about physical awkwardness and gaucheness (or strength and grace of course), and also how easy or hard it is to take initiatives or to follow somebody else's lead. It helps to teach us to observe someone else closely and in detail. This is valuable for our listening and counselling skills.

Section two – exercises for the main part of the session

Exercise 16   As a mother I am expected to . . .

Take a piece of paper and divide it into two columns. Head the left-hand column 'As a mother I am expected to . . .' and the right-hand column 'As a mother I . . .'. If you are working alone, divide up a page in your notebook, and put those headings on the two columns. The chances are that you will have an initial spate of points to write down, particularly in the 'expected to' column, but that by allowing quite a long time to think the headings over you will discover more and more of what you do do, and what pressures you experience.

Examples of the 'expected to' side that often come fairly quickly are: 'As a mother I am expected to be endlessly patient', 'As a mother I am expected to adore my baby', 'As a mother I am expected to know automatically everything about how to take care of a baby', 'As a mother I am expected to enjoy breastfeeding', and even 'As a mother I am expected to have given up sex'. On the 'As a mother I . . .' side, often fairly quickly come points like: 'As a mother I am still in my dressing gown at lunchtime', 'As a mother I am very tired', 'As a mother I feel very tender towards my baby', 'As a mother I feel very happy', 'As a mother I feel very vulnerable'. On further consideration more unexpected points may come up: 'As a mother I am expected to look after my children's teeth', 'As a mother I am expected to lose weight even though I feel hungry all the time', 'As a mother I am expected to be a frump', 'As a mother I am expected to be dedicated to family life', 'As a mother I feel pulled in a lot of directions at once', 'As a mother I wonder whether I shall ever have a clear head again', 'As a mother I feel more complete', 'As a mother I do not feel as grown up as I thought I would'.

After ten minutes, take it in turns to share with each other what is on your lists. You may like to talk around the points a bit, and talk about the differences between the contents of the two lists. It is a chance to get off your chest irritation and resentment about expectations, a chance to notice how and where you are as a mother — and the positive things you do as a mother come out and you have a chance to notice and enjoy them: 'As a mother I am very careful', 'As a mother I am good fun!', 'As a mother I do a lot of singing', 'As a mother I am good at understanding what my baby wants', 'As a mother I get more fresh air than I used to'.

Some of the expectations might be things you would like to achieve if you could clear up your block or tension about it. Helen, who said 'As a mother I am expected to take care of my children's teeth', had got into a tangle of feeling guilty and inadequate about getting teeth-cleaning and dentists' visits organised for her toddler. After talking about it, she felt she really did want to take care of those small teeth, and having had a chance to air her own fear of dentists, guilt about giving too many sweets to a restless child, and her own tiredness at the child's bedtime which made it hard to bother with routine teeth-cleaning, did manage to fix up a dental appointment and tackle the other toothy issues.

Alison had a similar experience with 'As a mother I am expected to teach my daughter to swim'. She felt that other mothers were so much more organised and everybody but her was managing to go to baby swimming classes (usually with whimsical titles like 'Water Babies' which she found an additional turn-off). This expanded to a rather larger feeling that everybody else was setting up a rich and interesting life for their babies and that she was 'too selfish' to do that. Nevertheless, after more thought she began to feel she would like to go swimming with her daughter and teach her to swim, so after a while they did join in a class.

Exercise 17　Messages

This exercise is another written one, and is about the messages our mothers gave us, and the messages we are giving to our babies. These messages may be obvious and spoken: 'Nice girls don't swear'; 'She's the pretty one, you're the clever one'; 'You're not a maternal person'; 'You're just like me'; 'I love you'. There are many other messages which are never spoken but which come through loud and clear: 'For heaven's sake don't ask me anything about sex'; 'It's a lousy deal being a woman'; 'I never had the freedom you've got'; 'You look tarty like that'; 'I'll always support you'; 'I enjoy your successes'. Have five quiet minutes to write about the messages you feel your mother gave, and perhaps any she still gives to you. If your mother died, or left you, this is all doubly hard. Write about any messages you can remember that your mother did give you, and then write about the messages you received from the people who cared for you after your mother became absent.

Now consider yourself and your baby. What messages are you giving to your baby? These are both spoken and unspoken: 'I love you', 'You wear me out', 'I'm frightened of you when you won't stop crying', 'I once nearly threw you on the floor at four o'clock in the morning', 'I hope you'll be happy', 'I just want you to know that life is alright and I hope you enjoy it as much as I do', 'I think you're beautiful', 'I'm delighted how strong you are', 'I'm looking forward to all the things we're going to do together', 'You irritate me', 'I want to understand you'. Have five quiet minutes to write down all the messages you feel you give to your baby. Take another few minutes to divide those messages into those which you are pleased to be giving, and those (if any) which you would like to stop giving. If there are additional messages that you would like to give but do not, at the moment, make a note of these too.

After that it is time to share what you discovered with your group. How the exercise feels to you of course depends on how things are for you with your mother, and how things are for you with your baby. If you feel shaky or distressed by the work, choose a support person, and let her hold your hand, put her hand on your shoulder, or put her arm around you, while you speak. The rest of the group should in this, as all other feedback in exercises, give you full, clear attention — avoid leaping in and trying to cheer you up, but give you support. It is cheering to notice supportive and affirmative messages we have had from our mothers, and saddening to focus on the rotten ones – the unfair criticism, the emotional blackmail, the envy. We may feel helpless rage looking at the contradictions among those maternal messages and wonder if we will ever shake off the resultant confusions. Unless you have a particularly sunny relationship with your mother it will probably make you feel fairly churned up. However, it is useful to look at some of the strands woven into that relationship.

When you have talked about messages from your mother to you, go on to describe the messages that pass from you to your baby. Explain which of these messages you are pleased to give and which you feel concerned about giving. Also describe any messages you would like to give, but do not feel you do at the moment: 'I wish I could tell him it's alright to be optimistic', or 'I wish I could feel calm and peaceful so that she could feel that I feel calm and peaceful, and she could feel calm and peaceful too'; 'I wish I wasn't bored so often. I think the baby picks up that I am peevish and bored especially in the afternoons, and it is very negative. He might think I am bored with him. I am not bored with him, I am bored with the life I am living at the moment. So I am concerned about giving him the message that I am bored'; 'I want to tell her clearly that the evening is my time. I don't want to see her after 7.30 in the evening – but I feel guilty about that so I keep going upstairs when she calls during the evening. I want to say I want the evenings in peace. Can you say that to an 8-month-old? Or is it cruel?'

If you are doing this exercise on your own, write the lists as described for a group, and give yourself time to reflect on them. You might like to make two drawings as well – a picture of yourself and your mother, and a picture of yourself and your baby. These drawings can give you more time and space to think and consider, and also give you a chance to express any emotions that are aroused. Finally, you cannot hope only to give wonderful, glowing, positive messages to your baby. Do not be horrified if some of the messages are negative. However, do use this as a way of seeing a little more clearly what is going on.

Exercise 18   *How has it changed?*

Treat this exercise as an opportunity simply to talk freely. Have three or four minutes each to talk about how your relationship with your mother has changed since your baby was born. Listen carefully to each other and enjoy sharing the interesting material which you will hear, and an uncritical audience while you speak. If you are working by yourself, give yourself time to write about the changes in your relationship with your mother since your baby's birth. Think carefully and write freely, then spend a little time reading over what you have written, and taking it in.

Exercise 19   *Who mothers you?*

We all need mothering at least some of the time; that is to say, we all need unconditional support, tenderness, cuddling, time and attention, some of the time. We all need someone who makes us feel special or gives us a small present or a hug from time to time, and someone to confide in who does not criticise. When you are a mother yourself you do not stop needing some mothering. In the group, have three or four minutes each to speak about where you get your mothering from. Who mothers you? The answer might be surprising. 'Actually,' said Anna, 'my mother does!' Not all mothers can though — absent or dead or estranged mothers clearly cannot, and complicated feelings about each other can get in the way. We need to have bits and pieces of mothering from all kinds of sources and put them together like a patchwork quilt: 'Susan often brings me flowers, and Jan listens to me, and Alan strokes my neck and shoulders when I'm tired.'

Women sometimes have a strange feeling that their babies mother them, and I am sure their babies sometimes do. It can have moments of being reciprocal. We may feel concerned that we do not want to coerce our children into looking after us all the time, and that might be an interesting point to notice – but it is usually just a touching and passing incident. Joanna described how she sat down one afternoon all worn out with looking after her 2-year-old and her 3-week-old baby. She felt unable to go on any longer, and began to cry. She did not sob because she did not want to frighten her toddler, but streams of tears flowed down her face. The little girl stared at her then went out of the room. She came back with a bucket and a large sponge, and tried to wipe away the tears with the sponge, and squeeze them out into the bucket! This marvellous and touching effort to take care of Joanna made her laugh through the tears and cheered her up. She was moved that her daughter was trying to help her and that she somehow recognised the extent of her upset by bringing a big bucket and a big sponge. Joanna said 'She looked as though she was going to mop up the tears of the whole world,' and felt that they were 'both in it together'.

Whatever reassurance-mothering you give your children will be reflected back to you when they are old enough to talk. Your own 'magic phrases' will come to you from them when you need help. When I look aghast or anxious my young children say to me 'We won't worry about that will we', which is exactly what I say to them. When they fall over they say 'Sort me out! Sort me out!' because I say to them 'Come on then, let's sort you out'. My young son touched me very much when he said, thoughtfully, 'I am a bit loving you'. It seemed such a careful way of putting it.

Working on your own, write about who mothers you, and how they do it.

Section three — exercises to close the session

Exercise 20   Rocking

So long as you have half a dozen people in your group you have enough to give each person in turn some rocking. It soon reminds you why babies like it so much; it is the most lovely feeling. The person who is going to be rocked should lie down on the floor. One person should kneel at her head and another at her feet; everyone else should kneel on either side of her. Cradling her head carefully lift her a few inches off the floor, the people along the sides sliding their arms right underneath her. Rock her gently — not from side to side but from the supporters' side to side (this sounds complicated but it is quite obvious when you do it). Watch her eyes close and a peaceful expression appear on her face. After a little while, lay her back down on the floor gently and let her wake up, gradually, before getting up and helping to rock someone else.

Exercise 21   Group hug

Get yourselves all close together and give each other a good hug.

On your own — you can hardly rock yourself or have a good hug by yourself. If you have a rocking chair or a hammock you can have some of the pleasant sensations of rocking, perhaps playing some calm and soothing music, as a way of closing your session. Another thought you might consider is having a massage sometime. It is expensive (£10.00 or more per session) but it could be a way of giving your body some good and uncomplicated attention. For six blissful months a friend of mine was training as a masseuse. 'Would it be an awful nuisance if I practised on you?' she used to ask. Needless to say I used to force myself to put up with it! If you need a relaxation to finish your session, do the relaxation described on p. 19, Exercise 12.

Exercise 22   Face massage

The person to be massaged should lie down on her back and relax. Her only task is to say if the person doing the massage is making her uncomfortable. If you are doing the massage, kneel at her head, one knee on each side of her. Take a moment or two to calm yourself, breathing away tension. Keep your own spine long and supple as you do the massage. Start by making long stroking movements from her chin up to the top of her skull, along both sides of her face and neck. Lift her head gently a fraction off the floor and lay it down again, the neck a little longer, the chin a little more tucked in. Get a feel of the shape of her skull. We have a kind of image of all skulls being the same, but they are all unique and different. Then, rest your hands lightly on either side of her forehead and stroke with your thumbs out to the side of her face. Smooth out her whole forehead two or three times; then with your fingertips make little circles at her temples – a few in one direction, a few in the other. Move your hands down and rest them lower down on the side of her face.

Stroke with your thumbs from the bridge of her nose out to the sides, and work down her face, stroking from the centre-line out. Smooth all the way down her face two or three times. Finish by making long strokes again from the chin up to the top of the skull, and then shake your hands out. Let her surface slowly from this lovely massage before you change around and each take the opposite role. When your time is over leave at least a week before you do the work in chapter 3. If you want to, record anything that seems important during the week, anything that occurs to you, any memory that suddenly comes back very clearly, any dream that seems to be asking to be remembered.

CHAPTER 3

Our Bodies – experiences, changes, and opportunities

What did childbirth do to your body? Take a deep breath as you think about that, relax your shoulders and breathe it away. Take your time if the thoughts come rushing helter-skelter. Well, sometimes it is a triumph. Some women feel the deepest poetry of their body has been properly expressed for the first time, and make a spontaneous and total physical recovery, and this, when it happens, is marvellous to see. Sadly, it is not that way for all of us. Many of us are unwarned, unfit, and completely unprepared for the impact of birth on our bodies. The initial feeling of lightness and relief after delivery gives way to horror when we realise just how much extra fat has accumulated on waist, bottom, thighs and arms.

In the weeks after delivery one's abdomen looks (and moves!) like a blancmange. If you were unlucky and got stretch marks it is a *wrinkled* blancmange. Ballooning breasts full of milk feel heavy but at least have a firm shape; when you stop breastfeeding you may be upset to find your breasts are much softer and less shapely than they were. In a world of page 3, strippergrams, and topless (an odd word for it) sunbathing, this can be shattering. In our group we found Gina Newsom's documentary, *Body Image* (Channel 4, 1986), an articulate and compassionate programme useful in expressing feelings we felt too furious or too inadequate or too miserable to get clear about. Sometimes episiotomies or tears are sewn too tight for sex to be comfortable afterwards, sometimes they are slow to heal and break down in infection after infection, leaving you feeling wounded, unclean, and unwell in your very womanhood. If the pain of labour was much worse than you anticipated, or you felt not properly supported or too much interfered with at the time of the birth, you may feel your whole body, and particularly your vagina, has been assaulted.

I will not forget what I felt as a 17-year-old mother who had put on far too much weight during pregnancy. Being fair-skinned and overweight my abdomen and thighs were covered with stretch marks. Overnight in hospital after the delivery my breasts became engorged, and when I woke they too were covered in angry red tiger-stripe stretch marks. I was scared to see this. An auxiliary nurse tried to reassure me and told me it was not dangerous, but added 'I am like you – all spoiled'. She didn't mean to be unkind and in fact meant to say she was just the same and it wasn't the end of the world. However, many women, I now know, share a feeling after childbirth of being irretrievably 'all spoiled'. This needs time, space, and sympathy to be properly expressed. It also needs someone to say all is not lost; if you are unlucky and put on too much weight and have a body that does not snap spontaneously back into shape, you can, when you feel ready, work on it yourself. In the middle section exercises of this chapter there are some suggestions for physical post-natal exercises, and re-commendations for books and videos that may help you.

The exercises in this chapter are the ones we have used to focus on our feelings about our bodies. You may like to take two sessions on this subject if it feels as though there is a great deal of material to look at here. For each session choose at least one exercise from each section – beginning, middle, and finishing exercises. If you use the video *Body Image*, use it as a middle section exercise, watching it together and then sharing your reactions to it.

Section one – exercises to begin the session

Exercise 23 *'In my next life . . .'*

This short exercise keys into your mood as you start your session. In your present frame of mind consider what animal you would like to be in your next incarnation. Go around the group sharing your idea and the reasons for it. Choose the first animal that comes into your head – its qualities probably have some message for you. 'In my next life,' said Sue with a look of uncharacteristic malevolence, 'I would like to be a tarantula. Then nobody would mess me around.' Other examples: 'I would like to be a leopard, because it's fast and fierce', 'I would like to be a penguin, then I could be as fat as I like and waddle around', 'In my next life I would like to be one of those sloth things that hangs upside down. I would like to sleep all day', 'I would like to be a hawk and see everything very clearly from the sky above'.

If you are working on your own, consider which animal you would like to be when you come back to the earth next time round. Try making a picture of the animal – not worrying about realism, concentrating rather on getting your feelings into the picture by the kinds of colours, pattern, and line that you use.

Exercise 24 *Short warm-up*

Give your body a gentle loosening warm-up. Stand with your feet hip-distance apart. Stand as tall as you can, tuck in your tail bone and lift your abdomen up and back towards your spine. Relax your shoulders. Breathing steadily, make two very slow big circles with your head. Pause for a moment with your chin on your chest, then make two big, slow circles the other way, finishing with your chin on your chest. Take a breath in, and on the breath out float your head up to the centre.

Check that your spine is still lifting, and abdomen lifted up and back towards your spine. Keep the back of your neck long. Make big circles with your shoulders, roll them backwards, slowly, four times, then forwards slowly four times. Lift your shoulders up – centre – down – centre four times, then forwards – centre – back – centre four times. Put your hands palm to palm in front of your chest. Keep your hips still, and slide your ribs to the right, bring them back to the centre, slide them to the left, then back to the centre. Breathe steadily, stand tall, and lift your abdomen up and back, as you move your ribcage across and back. Stretch four times each way.

Bend your knees a little and put your hands on your hips. Make very large, very slow circles with your hips. Use thigh, back, and abdominal muscles. Breathe steadily. Make four circles one way and four circles the other way. Straighten up. Stand your feet further apart – four feet or more – toes pointing forwards and feet parallel. Breathing in, stretch both arms straight upwards above your head, fingers together, palms facing front. Pull up tall on the waist. Breathe steadily. After a few seconds stretch forwards, head staying up. Bend at the tops of the thighs, not the back of the waist.

When you have stretched forwards as far as you can, start to sink downwards. If your hands reach the floor walk them back to be as close to the line between your feet as possible. If your hands don't reach the floor, hold onto opposite elbows with your arms, and the weight of your

arms pulls you a little further. Relax your head and neck.
Breathe steadily in the stretch. To come up, lift your head
up on a breath in. On the breath out, wriggle your feet in
until you come to a place where you feel safe to come up,
pressing both feet into the floor. Breathe out as you come
up, and roll your shoulders back a couple more times.

This short warm-up, easily accomplished alone or in a
group, stretches your muscles and improves your circu-
lation.

Exercise 25   Resilient arm exercise

This exercise comes from the Japanese martial art *aikido*,
which focuses on inner strength. To do this exercise you do
need to work with a friend. The exercise helps anyone who
is feeling physically flabby and weak by demonstrating how
strength comes first of all from within the spirit, and that
muscle power is an extra that can be added on later if we
want it. It also helps us to locate that inner strength.

Work with a partner. Stand facing her and, extending
your arm, place your wrist on her shoulder, palm up.
Clench your fist and brace the muscles of your arm tightly,
concentrating your thoughts on keeping your arm straight.
Now ask your partner to press down on the line of your
elbow to try to bend your arm. She should do this by
clasping her hands together and pushing down. Do your
best to stop her by tightening your muscles and concentrating hard. Stop either when she bends your arm or when
you feel tired. Shake your arm out well. Notice how this
felt.

Now try with a different kind of strength. Stand opposite
your partner and extend your arm. Rest your wrist on her
shoulder, palm up. Let your knees give a bit, and have a
feeling of 'grounding' your feet, with nice big footprints on
the ground. Now visualise it as rushing water – some see it

as warmth and light – flooding into you from *under* the ground, up through your legs, hips, chest and arms, and into your head. Particularly feel the power (light, warmth, rushing water) flooding through your arm. Relax your muscles and breathe slowly. Open your mind to the strength flowing through you. Ask your partner to try once again to bend your arm at the elbow, linking her hands together and pushing down on the crease in your inner arm where your elbow bends. Keep visualising the warm flow of power from under the ground up through you and into your arm. Keep it relaxed. Use the power of your partner's push as well – absorb it into your resilient arm.

Notice how it feels this time. You will probably be astonished to find that this open, relaxed strength is far stronger than the tight, contracted strength, and often it is quite impossible for your partner to bend your arm at all the second time. Now you know just how much power you have inside you, potentially anyway, by adjusting the relationship between your body and your mind. For a woman who has never thought of herself as strong, this can be a real discovery. Change around and try the exercise the other way round. When you are the arm-bender notice how different your partner's arm feels in the second part of the exercise.

Exercise 26 Pushing hands

With a friend or a partner in your group, stand facing each other with your feet hip-distance apart, and knees slightly bent. Rest your hands palm to palm. For a timed three or four minutes, experiment with pushing your hands against each other's. Afterwards allow time to tell each other how it felt. Did you feel pushed over and overwhelmed? Or did you push hard, wanting to push the other person around? Did your hands struggle against one another or play? Did you feel unsure what to do for some time, or start to move around easily?

Change partners and try again with a different person and see whether it feels similar or different. Use this exercise as a chance to explore your sense of physical power/powerlessness, your urge to be competitive, playful, or passive in your physical self.

Section two – exercises for the main part of the session

Exercise 27   Revisiting your experience of giving birth

Although at the time you may think you will never forget the experience of birth, it may start to slip away from you as the weeks pass. In this exercise we try to get in touch with our experience of childbirth once again.

It may be useful to bring your memories alive and into focus by seeing or reading of other women's experiences. The original 'Horizon' programme of Michel Odent's clinic at Pithiviers, *Birth Reborn* (BBC2), would be useful if hired on video. It has several lovely and moving births on it. For a group of women it may not be too expensive to hire. Documentaries about hospitals, midwives, and birth practices often show births, which always bring each woman's personal memories flooding back. Simply listening to conversations among women around you the following day will confirm that.

Here are some birth reports written by women in our group which, in their details and clarity, may also bring back some of the particular quality of your own experience.

Salli's first baby was born at home:

17/18 April: slept very badly indeed. Dreamt I had committed justifiable homicide. Tossed and turned all night trying to cope with the dream feelings; my first 'pregnant' dreaming.

19 April: slept better.

20 April: BIRTH DAY
6 a.m. – I couldn't sleep because I had terrible diarrhoea-like pains coming in waves. At first I made no connection with labour and just wanted to sleep. I slowly cottoned onto the fact that this was baby-associated but thought it was the 'overture' – effacement or something! The pains came in waves but were irregular and there was a permanent ache which made the whole thing unlike what I had expected of contractions.

9 a.m. – I rang Lesley for advice. She said it was definitely baby-associated, may well be labour but could go off.

9 a.m.–1 p.m. – The pains gradually became less like diarrhoea and I announced to Steve, 'This is pain'. I was still unsure about whether or not it was 'the real thing' as the pains were not great and very irregular – varying between every five to eight minutes, lasting forty-five seconds to one and a half minutes, though the height of the contraction was short-lived and at the beginning. I also had some backache which Steve eased by rubbing.

Steve was planning to go for a run but after some dithering we decided he had better hang around and finish decorating instead. (He was at home because it was a Bank Holiday.) He went to the shop to buy paint. I was coping with the pain by pacing the floor and rubbing my tummy low down. I didn't think it was very painful but wanted Steve with me so asked him to stop decorating. We spent some time doing the *Guardian* 'Quick Cross-word' (not very quickly). The pains gradually got more regular and stronger. We wrote down the timing of every one so we could really monitor what was happening. I decided to put on my birthing nightie and prepare the room so we went upstairs. Steve telephoned the midwife trying not to sound urgent as we didn't want to seem stupid!

1.50 p.m. – Barbara and Louise arrived. They said straight away that I wasn't too far along because I was still smiling. Vaginal exam – brilliant! I was 2–3 centimetres dilated and 'in labour'!! They seemed very pleased with my progress. The baby was posterior but somehow the fact didn't register with me. (It turned later on.) Barbara and Louise left. Steve and I carried on in the bedroom. I tried various positions but only wanted to pace the floor with Steve rubbing my back. Sometimes it helped to lean back on him but he had to keep rubbing my back and I had to keep walking!! I felt afraid of the pain to come as this was still bearable, though definitely painful. I never said 'contraction' – pain was a better description. I knew I was in labour but I couldn't believe the baby could come out! I wanted Steve by me every second. It irritated me if he wasn't there even for a fraction of a second. I remember hearing him bite his nail and I felt furious that he wasn't 'with me'. Other than that he was wonderful!

I continued to pace the floor. As the pains got greater I paced on the spot. I tried to sit in between but preferred to stand even when my legs ached and shook. I was fully conscious of everything even at the height of a contraction. At some point I had a 'show' – a bit late now I thought!

4 p.m. – Louise arrived and asked a few questions but didn't have a lot to do. I felt glad she was there. She said I was coping well and I felt proud! I had gradually got

more noisy with each pain. A couple of times I felt sick but I never was.

5.15 p.m. – Barbara arrived. I smiled to greet her between pains. The gaps were getting less. I was scared but it didn't make me wish the pains away; I had this knowledge that I had to get over them. I hoped I was 'getting somewhere'. I was unconscious of time but remembered I was missing a good film.

V.E. (vaginal exam) – I hated the idea of lying down. The first time I jumped up when the pain started. It was the worst moment of the whole thing. However, Barbara said I was 7 centimetres, up to 9 during a contraction. Barbara ruptured the membranes as they were still intact. Great! Steve asked how long until full dilation and Barbara said about an hour. I thought 'Oh no!', not realising how quickly the hours were going.

I don't know when the doctor arrived. I remembered being sorry I couldn't smile and say hello as I was in too much pain. I felt afraid of the transition that I knew was coming – what could be more painful than this! In fact, when it came I didn't recognise it and it was no worse than the few contractions before it. I got pushing feelings but didn't mention them because I thought I just wanted to go to the toilet – I hadn't expected the feeling to be identical to wanting to poo!! I was moving downwards into a semi-squat with each pain. My legs were shaking and I needed support. I had asked for gas and air thinking I was ages off transition. (Steve asked for it on my instructions.) With hindsight I'm sorry I did so because my notes show it was only twenty minutes before I was fully dilated. I still had 'one hour' ringing in my head. The pain was incredible for six or seven contractions (maybe more – memory unclear) and I didn't know what to do with myself. I hit the wall sometimes. I was also conscious of 'conducting' with my hands as if the pains were a musical score – I was 'riding over' them. I wish I had known I was in transition. I'm not sure how much the gas and air helped but once I had used it I didn't want to stop in case it was helping and the pain without it would be too much to bear. I also think I could have delivered in a squat position had I taken the opportunity. Even after lying down I should have got up when episiotomy was mentioned.

6.40 p.m. – *V.E.* I was *so scared* of having to lie down but the gas and air was helping a bit. I was dizzy and conscious of Barbara helping Steve support me but I never lost my sense of reality – even though they thought I did! Anyway, it was announced that I was almost fully dilated. Great! The pains immediately lessened so the V.E. wasn't as bad as I'd thought. I felt I could push but I never felt I *had* to push. Barbara suggested I carry on with the gas and air for a couple of contractions before I started to push. When I did push it relieved the pain so it seemed like a good idea. It took me a while to get the hang of pushing and I started to worry that having got this far I couldn't do it! Everyone was so encouraging and it really helped. I actually believed them when they said I was doing well! Finally I pushed 'into my bottom' in the right way. I knew it was right as soon as I did it. After that I just kept on pushing as long as the pains lasted. I had quite long breaks in between each pain which was nice. Steve was on one side of me and the doctor on the other – I was grateful to them both for being so strong. After some time Dr Trickett placed my own hands around my legs and suggested I control the pushes myself. I was reluctant to lose outside support but had a go and it worked quite well. I was sitting up against cushions but kept slipping down. All the time I didn't really know the baby would get out. I couldn't feel her moving along – only the pains and the strain of pushing – though I was thinking about the baby all the time. I was kept informed of how I was doing but didn't think being able to see 2 inches of the baby's head was very encouraging! I thought I'd never get her out. For the first time I felt Steve was losing interest in me and looking for the baby. I didn't mind too much as I needed him less now. Quite often I remembered the terrible transition pains and felt glad they were over.

They started discussing an episiotomy. The doctor was obviously in favour. I could hear Steve questioning it and was grateful though I was past caring. I think I nodded my agreement so they went ahead. It was only a small cut they told me! After that the baby seemed to come charging out. I opened my eyes for the first time in ages and her head had been born!! I was thrilled and couldn't believe it. I did a couple more pushes and she was born (8 p.m.) What a joy!! Up onto my tummy. She was breathing and gurgling. I'd done it! She was all slimy but beautiful. I asked if it was a boy or a girl. I remember thinking I wouldn't care but when they said a girl I was overjoyed. The doctor took photographs.

Third stage went quickly with one push and a bit of tugging from the doctor. I felt really pleased to have done it without syntometrine so the cord didn't need to be cut until it had stopped pulsating. (In the event I had to have the injection later as I was losing too much blood, but it didn't matter then.) The doctor stitched me up. Ouch! It was great being at home. The three of us were not separated from birth onwards. Barbara, Louise, Dr Trickett and Steve were all fantastic. I was pretty good too! And Helen is lovely.

Jane had a happy and fulfilling delivery in hospital:

JANE MACKINNON – Second pregnancy (first delivery was full of complications, including pethidine, epidural, forceps and episiotomy and finally a beautiful daughter). This time I was determined to try and deliver my baby naturally.

Jamie Scott MacKinnon born at 4.15 p.m. on 2 July 1987 (7 lbs 0 ozs).

Wednesday 1 July: Ten days late and feeling rather heavy and lethargic, had a whisky and a cry at bedtime but managed to sleep with only one obligatory pee during the night!

Thursday 2 July: Awoke 7.30 a.m. Had a cup of tea and cereal as usual. Felt very slight discomfort rather like an extremely mild period pain, I desperately hoped that it just might be labour pains at last. During the next hour or so I went to the loo several times and hoped that perhaps this was the body preparing for the big event, but pains still not really positive so decided to have a hot bath and try not to make too much of things. The pains continued in the bath and became more regular, about once every five to ten mins. but still not uncomfortable enough to require a special position or breathing. After my bath I went to the loo yet again and discovered that I had a very slight streaked discharge but only enough to call the suspicion of a show. My own feelings were still uncertain but now a little more optimistic. I decided to watch the rest of 'Good Morning Britain' and finish my knitting (the last sleeve of a matinee coat!). I finished and still the twinges were coming every five minutes and now needing some controlled breathing. Fortunately Iain was on 2–10 shift and was therefore still at home, we decided that this might be the start of something and each time I got a pain Iain timed it, they lasted about forty seconds and were still every five minutes. With the breathing I felt really in control and could not believe that this was really it. I decided to dust the lounge to keep busy (a most unusual thing for me to do on a sunny morning!). Each time a pain came I breathed, dusted and wriggled my hips, but still completely in control and Iain and I got the giggles each time as it all seemed so exciting and unreal. This remedy of dusting and wriggling took me through till 12.00 noon, the only thing that worried me was the noticeable lack of movement from the baby, so I decided to phone the 'Princess Anne' and the Sister suggested that I go in and let them check that all was well and to confirm that I really was in labour. We arrived there at about 12.30 p.m. and were taken to room 12 (a blue room – could this be significant?). Here I was given the glamorous NHS nightie and asked for a sample and details so far. When I collected my specimen I discovered it contained some fresh blood and a small clot about the size of a 10p coin. This rather worried me but the midwife assured me that this was probably due to my being in labour rather than anything to worry about. Next I was placed on the monitor which proved slightly unreliable, needing the occasional prod to keep it recording properly, rather unnerving at times! After the monitoring was completed a doctor came to examine me, she said I was at least 5 cms dilated and that she would rupture the now bulging membrane, as soon as she had done this I went straight to 7 cms and was left once again to my own devices. The pains now increased in intensity and I asked for a beanbag which was really comforting to have, I knelt up facing it and Iain rubbed my back and held a cold wet compress hard against my forehead during the now very strong contractions, but I was still in control using the very deep breathing and an occasional bite on the beanbag. The student midwife and student health visitor who were in the room with us were most encouraging and kept on saying how well I was doing. This did wonders for my confidence and very soon I was in transition. I decided to turn and have the bean bag at my back and have a go with the gas and air, amazing stuff, using this with the breathing at the beginning of each contraction I got through the transition stage without realising it and soon my body was making involuntary pushing actions at the end of each one – my thoughts then went back to our sessions and I asked whether someone should check that I was fully dilated. The midwife said that this was not necessary as it was obvious that I was ready and that I could go ahead and push (the room had now filled up somewhat with a variety of students all of whom were gathered at my rear end like cheer leaders!). The gas and air was put away and I was told to give three pushes with each contraction. This I found very difficult because I felt that I was going to burst if I pushed any harder than I already was. Iain was really marvellous during all this and had one arm around my shoulders and the other behind my thigh helping me push each time. I remember saying several times that I was sorry but I didn't think I could do this but after much encouragement I got my baby 'round the bend' and the midwife put my hand down and I could feel my baby's head waiting to come out and at last I really believed I could do it – all that fuss about nothing! Now I was told to put my chin on my chest and push again and then pant. This I did and the head came out – WOW! What a feeling, and then I was helped to look down and saw my baby for the first time, patiently waiting for the next contraction which soon came and he came slithering out, just as Paddy had said – Jamie Scott had arrived and it was still only 4.15 p.m. We were really ecstatic. He was quickly checked by the midwife then handed to me for a first cuddle during which the placenta was delivered so easily that I really did not notice it – it looked horrible because it was calcified, not only that but Jamie's cord was in a knot, fortunately only a loose one! The worst part was next as I had a tear which had to be stitched, but this did not last long and soon I was supping tea with Iain after which I had a refreshing bath and Iain cuddled Jamie. After my bath we were left alone again in the delivery room so that I could feed Jamie for the first time.

For Sarah, childbirth was a fairly horrible experience in spite of her careful preparation and positive expectations:

It all began at 11.30 p.m. 17 December, half an hour after my return from listening to the *Messiah* at the Guildhall, with a 'show' which wasn't blood-streaked as the books suggest so I was a bit confused. I went to bed, but an hour later couldn't get comfortable, though not really in pain, and went to the loo about 1 a.m. I knew at once this was the waters breaking because it all gushed out and I had no control over it at all – most disconcerting! I was still a bit bewildered though, since I clearly wasn't getting contractions and it seemed that my plans to stay at home as long as possible were being thrown. Sure enough, the phone call to the hospital meant I had to go in straight away, so while Roger panicked and went to find an all-night garage (I was so certain the baby would be late!), I quite calmly started packing the case which should have been waiting.

Arrival at the hospital was unceremonious – the doors were locked and no-one was in a terrible hurry to let us in. Nervous as I was by this time, I was not put at my ease from being examined by a doctor whose English was far from perfect and the decision to send me up to the ante-natal ward and Roger home for a few hours upset me further. It was all a bit of a nightmare – I was in a ward with two other people who weren't in labour and were obviously trying to sleep, while I was getting contractions every fifteen minutes or so which, though really no more than cramp-like period pains, were enough to stop me sleeping and make me want to walk around.

Morning finally came, but breakfast didn't, and four of us were collected and herded down the corridor to the labour ward, our baggage before us on a wheelchair, like lambs to the slaughter. I was very anxious for Roger to arrive by this time and felt much happier when, about 10.30 a.m., the three of us were installed and waiting for action.

The first examination of the day pronounced me 2–3 cms dilated on my own, so it was agreed I should be left to get on with it until about 12.30 when they'd re-assess and consider putting me on a drip to augment. It did make a difference at last being treated as someone in labour and Dr Peter Huntingford's phrase 'the dignity of labour' really could be applied to those first few hours. The contractions were painful but bearable and being able to walk about, lean on things and people, sit, kneel, rock etc. were all very helpful. The breathing was fine and Caroline helped me, but relaxing through the pain was just not on. I've been doing those exercises at yoga as well as the special classes for years, but I think the unpredictability of it for a first-time mother and therefore the fear of the unknown make relaxation well-nigh impossible.

By 12.30 I was pronounced only 3 cm and contractions only every three minutes so the decision was made to put me on the drip. On reflection I wonder if I might have refused this, but I'd have made myself very unpopular and the argument about risk of infection seemed fairly persuasive. However, I think it was at this point that any possibility of a bearable or enjoyable labour fled.

At 3.30 I was pronounced 5–6 cms, which was supposed to be consoling, but in fact reduced me to tears for the umpteenth time that day. In my defence I should add that I had not slept well on Monday night, had had an absurdly busy day on Tuesday, was in labour by Tuesday night and had not slept at all and not eaten since 6 p.m. Tuesday. By this point on Wednesday, then, I was at a pretty low ebb, and was put on a saline and glucose drip.

It was Roger who really persuaded me at 4 o'clock to have a shot of pethidine – since I was not coping at all well with the fairly constant pain and he was finding it hard to watch. In the end it was probably a good move, though its power to deal with the pain seemed very limited. Its value seemed to me to lie in distancing me from the event so that I couldn't help relaxing *between* contractions and mounting panic could not take over. Not long after I was finally allowed gas and air, which really was a godsend – by then I'm afraid I was beginning to feel I'd rather die than go through another contraction and I began to wonder whether being told one needed a Caesarean might be the biggest relief in the world.

I don't remember transition at all. On the bed for another examination, I remember Roger starting to sponge my face in between my diving for the mask and cursing for not using it quite early enough each time, and then someone saying 'She's going to want to push quite soon'. According to Roger it was only about fifteen minutes from this point to the point at which I realised I was never going to push her out in that position and asked to kneel up. The midwife sounded unhappy, not to say scandalised, to me, but the Sister by this time present simply busied herself organising the sag bag. They didn't give me an episiotomy either since I apparently sounded like I meant it when I said no – and indeed I think it would have been the last straw for me after all the intervention there'd been so far – not that a second-degree tear being stitched up afterwards was pleasant and I don't know even now whether I was right.

Once kneeling at the end of the bed, a couple of terrifyingly violent pushes where I thought my whole body would split in half and Isabelle exploded into the world. It could not by any stretch of the imagination be called a controlled delivery and the photograph of her blood-splattered and as if having been dropped from a great height is a fairly accurate reflection of the event.

I was shattered, sore and semi-conscious, but awake enough to count the fingers and toes, cuddle her and give her a first taste of the breast before passing out completely. I'd have to say I was glad it was over, found childbirth a rather violent and very painful experience, but of course I'm glad to have done it – or at least, glad to have the result of it all. It makes you realise, though, what a liberating thing is efficient contraception.

Although many women have happy experiences of birth with the aid of an epidural anaesthetic, Jennifer had very mixed feelings about it afterwards and has quite sad memories of the delivery itself:

By 29 March, my baby was eight days late and I was desperate – what was I doing wrong? Why wouldn't he be born? However, on that day (ironically – Mother's Day) I had a show, and the contraction pains started. Alan and I were ultra-cool – went to the cinema to see *A Room with a View* – timing my contractions in the dark. Came home, cooked a full roast dinner – timing my contractions over the cooker. By 9 p.m. they were getting very painful and coming irregularly, but about every three minutes. I had a bath, phoned the hospital, who were not particularly keen that I came in but they were so painful I decided on going. On arrival I was examined and woe – was only 2 cm dilated. The midwife knew I wanted an active birth and perhaps because of that seemed rather remote – left Alan and me to do our own thing and didn't offer much help or support. We spent the next two hours doing the breathing I had learned at active birth classes – 'breathe in peace . . . breathe away pain . . .' – this helped somewhat although I couldn't find any position to relieve the pain. I tried standing/sitting/on all fours . . . nothing helped. It did help, though, to have a partner to guide me through the breathing. By about 2 a.m., I was 5 cm dilated, and had had enough! I asked for pethidine . . . it made me feel very sleepy and woozy but didn't really take the pain away. As it wore off, the pain became intense and frightening. Everyone said I was doing marvellously well but I felt awful and really had had enough this time. I was 7 cms dilated by about 5 a.m. . . . the midwife asked if she could break my waters – which she did. This wasn't painful at all. By 7 a.m. I was still only 7–8 cms dilated and feeling exhausted and miserable. My cervix was apparently slightly puffy and inflamed which was holding up the dilation, and the baby was OP* and not rotating. I asked for an epidural . . . simply because I felt I couldn't go on any longer. I felt very bad about doing this. Clearly the midwife and my partner were hoping I could manage without and although no-one said anything I felt their disapproval (this, of course, could all be in my imagination but I think not). The midwife was great – kept checking me right up until the last moment before the epidural in the hope that I would have dilated some more and it wouldn't be necessary – but there was no progress. The epidural doctor

* Occipital presentation, i.e. with the back of the head facing forward.

was charming. I remember a highly lucid conversation about Wendy Savage, active birth and the psychology behind men going into obstetrics! I was fortunate in that the epidural worked very well – I had total pain relief and no after effects such as headaches.

However, once the epidural was in, it started a chain of events I really hadn't bargained for in my wildest dreams. I had to lie flat so my contractions stopped (this had been the case in the last two weeks of pregnancy – the Braxton Hicks contractions always stopped when I lay down). My blood pressure dropped dramatically and so did the baby's heartbeat rate. I was put on a drip to stimulate the contractions and a scalp monitor checked the baby's heartbeat, which wasn't holding up well. Clearly, people were concerned. Three doctors appeared from nowhere, and a blood sample from Luke's scalp revealed that he was in danger of oxygen starvation. The drip concentration was turned up . . . two more blood samples taken . . . murmurings of a Caesarean if I didn't begin to dilate more. I asked to be sat up. I believed this would help the contractions. It seemed to work and by 1 p.m. (five hours after the epidural had been given at 8 a.m.) I was 9 cms dilated.

Suddenly the doctor decided that he could see Luke's head, and despite the fact that he was still OP, and still not rotating, he would try a forceps delivery. Once the decision was made, action was rapid. Rotating forceps were used and because of the epidural this was totally pain-free for me. My partner stood by my head holding my hands and, at my request, talking fast and furious about his work problems. A team of thousands seemed to appear once Luke was delivered – he needed oxygen, and a stomach wash, since there was meconium present as he was delivered. However, after two or three minutes we heard a cry – then a yell – and were reassured his lungs were in working order! I was sewn up immediately. I had a large episiotomy – and Luke fed after twenty minutes or so.

In retrospect, I feel very sad that I succumbed to the lure of the epidural, and wasn't able to manage by myself. However, the pains were much more intense than I had imagined they would be. I don't know whether this is because I'm a coward or because I did have a genuinely difficult birth. I do believe that the epidural took the birth out of my hands. As I said, it set in chain a whole sequence of events which I hadn't bargained for.

The birth of Jo's baby needed medical intervention, but everything was so sensitively done, and she felt so involved in all the decisions, that the birth was a happy experience:

I'd had two weeks of 'one off' contractions, just when I was beginning to think that I was going to spend the rest of my life pregnant! (Although I wasn't due for another week.) Saturday was spent feeling extremely constipated. I hardly ate a thing and because Laurie felt the same I put it down to something we had eaten. Previously in the week I had tried a dose of castor oil, as I'd been told it sometimes got things started! (Christmas was getting nearer!) However, nothing happened. This time I was really constipated so I tried again.

At 12.30 a.m. Laurie and I went to bed, but I couldn't sleep due to increasing backache. I just had to get up and walk about. I went to the loo at 1.15 a.m. and saw blood, I took this to be a show and quietly got excited. At about 2.30 a.m. I had a small but definite contraction. I tried to go to bed as I would need some sleep if I was due to start labour, but every time I lay down I had backache. I went downstairs and made Laurie some sandwiches ready for the hospital. At 3.15 I had another contraction, I leant against the wall and swayed my hips, however it was not painful. On going to the loo I noticed more blood and became concerned that perhaps it was heavier than it should have been. At 4.15 I decided to wake Laurie, I'd let him sleep on so that he would be as fit as possible when his energy was really needed. He suggested I phone the hospital to see what they said. The woman on duty felt that it was just a heavy show and told me to take paracetamol and get as much sleep as I could. At 4.25 I had another contraction. I lay on the bed on all fours and swayed my hips while Laurie massaged my back. I remembered my breathing and found that it really did work! My contractions were coming every twenty minutes or so and lasting fifteen to twenty seconds. Then they increased in frequency to every ten minutes. At 5.45 they had increased to every seven minutes.

I phoned the hospital at 5.45 to say that we were on our way. At 6.00 we left. En route to the hospital they came every four minutes.

We arrived at the hospital at 6.20 a.m., my contractions were coming fast but I felt I was coping with them. Going down the corridor of the labour ward contractions were coming every two minutes, I leant against the wall as we walked along. At 6.30 a.m. we were in the labour room. On phoning earlier I had reminded the staff that I hoped to have an active birth and would like a low bed.

I was wired up to the monitor for the twenty-minute examination. I was then examined and found to be 4 cms dilated already. Then the monitor was taken off and we were told to feel free to walk around if we wanted. My contractions were coming fast so I lay on the bed. I buried my head in the bean bag and swayed my hips whilst breathing long and slow. I was sweating profusely and asked to take the gown off. This made me feel much more comfortable and free. Laurie massaged my back throughout the contractions and was soothing and encouraging.

At 9.00 a.m. I was examined again and found to be 9 cms. The midwife was becoming concerned about my blood pressure which was increasing. This has been a problem throughout my pregnancy. My waters had still not broken though the midwife said they were at breaking point, and asked if I would like them broken. I said that I would rather wait a while longer so long as everything else was OK. At 9.30 a.m. I agreed to have my waters broken. It was at this point that the midwife saw meconium in the waters, they immediately fixed me to the monitor. The baby showed no signs of distress. From then on I wore the monitor although I was still free to move and spent most of the time on all fours. I was aware of Laurie and the midwife talking but couldn't concentrate on what they were saying. I was concentrating on 'going with' the contractions not fighting them. The midwife told us that my cervix was not pulling back.

At 9.45 a.m. I began the second stage and pushed with the contractions. I was on all fours except for when being examined. This was the hardest part, I put all my energy into pushing and was not getting any results. I was offered gas and air but was determined to do without, I was secretly feeling pleased with myself for getting that far unaided. My blood pressure was still increasing and was being tested frequently. The doctors were becoming increasingly concerned and felt that forceps might be needed. At this point I was advised to try sitting upright bearing down, putting my hands at the back of my thighs and my chin to my chest. I had now been pushing for an hour, I was beginning to feel giddy and nearly fainted. The baby's heartbeat still seemed strong and I felt it reassuring to have the monitor on.

I asked Laurie what we should do, he told me to do as I wanted but I could see that he was starting to worry. I agreed to forceps as there was no sign of the head and I'd been pushing for an hour and ten minutes. I insisted on continuing to deliver myself whilst the forceps were being set up, and was encouraged to do so by both Laurie and the staff. Even with the forceps I felt that the baby would never come out. I gripped Laurie's arm and buried my head in his chest in between the contractions. At each contraction I beared down. At last the head was visible, everyone was encouraging me, telling me how well I was doing and that I would soon have my baby. In between contractions I had been told that the baby would have to be put on the resuscitator and sucked out straight away. All of a sudden I could feel the head, see the cord and shoulders, our baby had made it, a girl. The staff were as quick as possible to clear her out and give her to me. This took about twenty minutes as a lot had been swallowed, but soon she was in my arms and suckling. I had done it.

It would have been fantastic to have a completely active birth in the sense that I would have delivered on all fours, but I do not feel disappointed – I had held out as long as possible, and in the end circumstances determined my decision to have forceps: the baby beginning to show signs of distress, my increasing blood pressure, and I had been pushing for eighty minutes, nearly twice as long as average. It was active birth to me, I made the decisions at every point, and I did it without drugs.

It may be a cliché but none the less true, when I say that giving birth to Lauren was an experience that was wonderful and the memory of which will stay with me forever, the pain and the joy.

After reading through these varied accounts take time to tell the story of your own baby's birth. You will be fascinated listening to each other – listen to yourself carefully too and absorb your impressions and feelings, and what sights, sounds, smells, and details have stayed with you. In your confidential group you do not have to idealise or sanitise your birth story. Enjoy the freedom of being able to say what you mean, and discover whether you really did enjoy it, or really did hate it, and whether the things you are in the habit of saying about the birth still ring true.

If you are working alone, spend some time travelling back in your imagination to the time of your baby's birth. Now write your birth story down in your book, illustrating it with drawings, or decorating it with patterns if you like to.

Exercise 28   What has changed?

In a group, have five minutes (timed) each. Speak about any changes you have noticed in your body, and also about any changes you have noticed in your sexuality. Be as open or as private as feels right for you, there is no need to say anything which you do not wish to share. This gives each woman an opportunity to voice any worries she has and to exchange views and information. For information about your body, invest in a copy of *Our Bodies Ourselves* by the Boston Women's Health Book Collective. For understanding and information about post-natal sexual difficulties look at the relevant chapter of Sheila Kitzinger's excellent *Woman's Experience of Sex*. Find out if there is a local Well Woman Clinic for help with any lingering physical problems, and practise some assertiveness (see chapter 4) if it feels difficult to get clear information and advice from your GP.

If you feel shaky or distressed when it is your turn to talk, choose a support person, as in previous exercises, and ask for whatever support you would like (for her to sit next to you, or hold your hand, or put her arm round you) while you speak. It's almost a truism about group work, but it really does help to hear about other people's experiences – for example, of loss of desire, or fear of loss of desirability – to compare notes on persistently sore stitches or scars, on how to manage post-natal contraception. It's useful to know that everybody else's baby, like yours, wakes and yells as soon as any passion sparks into life in your bed. They seem to be fitted with quite efficient anti-sex radar. It's useful just to know that everybody else hasn't necessarily got everything under control. It means a lot to know you are not alone, and sometimes even gives you the first glimpse of a feeling there might eventually be improvement, growth, positive change.

Working alone, record in your book any changes you find in your body after birth, and any changes in your sexuality and your sex life. Remind yourself that you are describing how things are, how things feel, now. Things can change, and any unhappiness need not necessarily be permanent.

Exercise 29   Favourite and unfavourite

Almost all women have an unfavourite part of their bodies. Grimacing horribly they will name anything from head to toes as an offending part: 'It's my nose that's the problem really', 'My eyes are too small', 'My mouth's a funny shape', 'My hands are so square and stubby', 'My arms are fat', 'My elbows are lumpy', 'My breasts are too small/too big/not a good shape', 'My stomach's revolting', 'My bottom/my thighs/my ankles/my feet are horrible, horrible, horrible'. This is a deafening chorus. I have been disturbed to hear how many women have fantasies about mutilating their bodies. Lorraine said 'I used to think about getting a knife and carving away my ankles until they were nice and thin.' She did not ever seriously intend to do this but had harboured the fantasy for years. Other women speak of similar fantasies about slicing supposedly excess fat off waist and thighs. It seems a grim indictment of the acute pressure on women to conform to fashionable body-types that many ruefully acknowledge thoughts of carving themselves to pieces. I suspect few women will have any difficulty nominating a 'least favourite' part of their bodies.

What about your favourite part? When asked what the favourite part of their bodies is, women often succumb to a wave of modesty and choose a really tiny part – like their thumbnails! However, if your thumbnails really are your favourite part, stick with them.

To do the exercise in the group, work with a partner. In these paired exercises, keep changing partners so you work with as many different people as you can and avoid getting into little cliques. Have five minutes each to speak about the least favourite and most favourite parts of your body. Talk about the qualities you enjoy or dislike in those parts: 'I like my eyes. I think they really are the windows of my soul. I like their colour, they are greeny brown, a rich autumny colour'; 'I like my legs. Whatever else seems to go peculiar in my body, my legs stay long and smooth. They're strong, I can run well and kick well. I can look after myself with my legs and I like the way they look'; 'I like my lips. They're a very particular shape. They're an interesting shape. I think my personality is quite like my mouth – lively and particular'; 'I'm fond of my hair. My hair is thick and curly, it doesn't cost me a lot of time or effort or money!'

Working alone, write about your most favourite and least favourite parts of your body. Write all about feelings and associations about them, taking plenty of space.

Exercise 30 I'm kind to my body/unkind to my body

Do you treat your body as an enemy or a friend? Take a piece of paper and divide it into two columns. Head one side 'I'm kind to my body' and the other side 'I'm unkind to my body'. Have five minutes (timed) to write in both columns: 'I'm kind to my body by going swimming', '. . . by eating lots of fresh fruit', '. . . by doing yoga every day', '. . . by using lots of body lotion!', '. . . by going running', '. . . by getting a good sleep'; 'I'm unkind to my body by smoking too much', 'I'm unkind to my body by hating it', 'I'm unkind to my body by going on and off diets all the time'.

Then go around your group sharing the contents of your lists. Take notice of anything that surprises you or calls for your attention. Women working alone can divide a page of their notebooks in half and take five minutes to write in both columns. Read your writing through afterwards and take in what you have discovered. Notice which column has more items in it.

Exercise 31 Short exercise programme

You are faced with an unenviable project, called by magazines, clinics, and a great deal of women themselves, 'getting your figure back'. A proportion of women instantly react – 'What about me? I didn't have a figure in the first place.' The GP weighs you at your six-week check, and acquaintances all comment, to your face, 'Ooh, you've got back quickly haven't you?', and behind your back, 'Honestly, she's *twice* the size she was!' Unless you have 'got your figure back' you will be only too aware of pre-baby clothes that you were looking forward to wearing, hanging uselessly in the cupboard because they are too tight. You are so sick of your maternity clothes that you probably burned them at the full moon anyway, and this leaves you borrowing shirts and jeans from male friends and partners, or being limited to loose outfits. For a few women the problem is the other way around and many months of breastfeeding and general hard work leave them painfully thin. Those of us who tend towards heaviness may hoot with derision — I particularly hate watching an underweight friend of mine forcing down cake at coffee time to build herself up a bit! — but I should not have such an insensitive attitude. Being underweight leaves you tired, weak, and prone to infection, and it is important to build yourself up with a good balanced diet of nutritious food, and take your GP's advice about iron and vitamin supplements.

Number of pounds weight is not the only issue. A slack abdomen is uncomfortable, a slack vagina can leave you dissatisfied and miserable sexually. Tense shoulders and an aching lower back are also common. All of these conditions can be improved by exercise. If you can invest in books or tapes you may find them useful in encouraging you to do exercise instead of just meaning to do it. Exercise does work — all you've got to do is actually do it!

Post Natal Exercise by obstetric physiotherapists Margie Polden and Barbara Whiteford sets out an organised programme, building up from the day after delivery to six months afterwards. Jane Fonda may make you cringe when she urges you to 'Burn off those love handles', but she has written frankly about food, exercise, and strength for women, and shared her own experiences helpfully and fully. Her *Workout Book for Pregnancy, Birth and Recovery* has a sensible 'Recovery Workout', and a tape of the exercises counted out to music is also available. In both those books the women photographed doing the exercises are obviously post-natal — so you are not looking at pictures of slender nymphs, but of women who, like you, have heavy breasts full of milk and a tummy still a little swollen. This helps you to keep going, as does the fact that they look cheerful, relaxed, and as though they are really getting somewhere.

Stretch and Relax, by Maxine Tobias and Mary Stewart, is a marvellous book with which you could begin yoga at home. It has an ante-natal section, and then a post-natal section from which you could gradually build up onto the original beginners' programme. Yoga offers a form of exercise which can gradually spread a feeling of flexibility, strength, and peace through the whole of your life.

This short exercise programme gives you a set of exercises to do every day, to keep you going until you come to a decision about getting to a class or organising yourself into swimming, running, dancing, or one of the post-natal exercise programmes. If you don't want to or never get around to any of those noble pursuits, the programme should help the crucial muscle groups. You can do this short programme any time from two weeks past delivery – six weeks if you had a Caesarean. If your post-natal bleeding gets significantly heavier after exercise you are overdoing it – if it gets heavier anyway in ordinary life you are overdoing it too. Listen to that message and try to rest a little more. If you ever have a sudden heavy flood of blood (running down your legs even if you are wearing a pad) ring your GP, maternity hospital or casualty department immediately and get attention at once.

Start with the 'Short warm-up' Exercise 24 then do a *side stretch*. Stand with your feet 3 to 3½ ft apart, left foot turned in, right foot turned out. Check that your right heel is in line with your left instep. Breathing in, lift your arms out to the side shoulder level. Breathing out, drop your shoulders and stretch your fingertips even further out. Take another breath in and on the breath out stretch away to the

Side stretch

right and then come down, resting your right hand on knee, calf or foot. Stretch your left arm straight up, palm facing front, fingers together. Look up at the upper thumb with the lower eye. Take five slow breaths in and out. Breathing in, come up, and breathing out, let your arms sink down to your sides.

Now make your side stretch to the other side. Come down onto all fours, hands shoulder-distance apart, knees hip-distance apart.

Cat stretch. On a breath out arch your back up, slowly and stretchily, like a cat. Scoop your abdomen upwards towards your spine. On a breath in flatten your back. Repeat six times.

Cat balance. On a breath out stretch out your left arm

Frog stretch

and right leg. Hold for a few steady breaths, then slowly lower hand and knee. Stretch the other side, then slowly lower hand and knee. Repeat each side six times.

Hip circles. Still on all fours, slowly circle your hips, using back, thigh and abdominal muscles. Make six big slow circles in one direction, and six in the other direction.

Frog stretch. Separate your knees and put your feet together. Sit back on your heels. Breathe in, and on a breath out walk your hands forwards along the floor. Make your spine as long as you can. Inch your fingers further along the floor, and let your head sink down between your upper arms towards the floor. Really stretch.

Now fold your arms and rest your head on your arms. Contract and release your pelvic floor muscles a dozen times. If you do no other exercise do this and do it all your life. The pelvic floor muscles – (the hammock of muscles around the area that would be covered by a sanitary pad) are crucial for women. If you stand up you'll notice that they are what is holding your insides in! You have just added the weight of baby, placenta, and waters to the strain, and then pushed a baby out through them, maybe they were torn or cut in the process. You must look after them! Squeeze and release the muscles a dozen times during your exercise time, and half a dozen times any time it crosses your mind day or night (you don't have to get down into the frog stretch to do this).

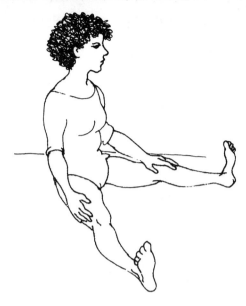

Stretch your legs wide apart and push your heels away . . .

. . . then bring the soles of your feet together and let your knees stretch slowly down to reach the floor.

If you are down in the frog stretch, breathe in and lift your head up, breathing out walk your hands towards you and sit right up.

Sitting stretches. Sit tall, pulling your bottom back to make sure you're sitting on the centre of your pelvic floor. Lift your spine, and keep the back of your neck long. Now stretch your legs wide apart and push your heels away. Rest the backs of your hands on the fronts of your knees. Take five slow, steady breaths in and out in this stretch, then bring the soles of your feet together and let your knees stretch slowly down towards the floor. Take five slow and steady breaths in and out here too.

Hero pose. Kneel with your knees together and feet apart. Slowly sit down between your feet. If your knees feel too tight put a couple of cushions between your feet and start again. Link your hands together, push your palms away, and then stretch your arms up over your head. Stay there for five slow breaths in and out. Float your arms back down. Now link your hands behind your back and on a breath out stretch forward, think about lying down along your thighs. Let your arms float up behind you. You will not lift them far at first, eventually you will lift them vertically behind you.

Lying down. Lie on your back. Stretch out your left leg and bend your right knee onto your chest. Lifting your head and neck off the floor take your left elbow to your right knee. Now change right round, take right elbow to left bent knee and stretch your right leg out. Breathing out hard with each movement alternate from right to left in this 'bicycling' exercise. Build up gradually to thirty-six repetitions. Picture your abdomen pressing down towards the floor.

Stretch both legs vertically up, then let them stretch wide apart. On the breath out lift your straight legs and cross them at the ankles, breathing in stretch your legs wide apart. Picture your abdomen pressing down towards the floor. Build up to twenty-four repetitions. Hug your knees to your chest for five deep breaths.

Relax your arms on the floor by your sides. Bend your knees and put your feet flat on the floor hip-distance apart. On a breath out push your hips up and on a breath in lower your hips to a couple of inches off the floor. Don't let your back arch. Lift and lower your hips, building up to twenty-four repetitions. Then spread your feet wider apart and lift and lower, building up to twenty-four repetitions. Next, push your hips up and keep your hips up while you bounce your knees together and apart, up to twenty-four times. Lastly, bring knees and feet together and lift and lower your hips twenty-four times (a smaller movement, this one). Now hug your knees to your chest again for five slow breaths.

Relax quietly for a few minutes as in the 'Deep relaxation' Exercise 12.

Section three – exercises to close the session

Exercise 32   A decision

Having spent some time thinking carefully about your body, do you feel ready to make any decision, small or large, about your body, your fitness, or your health? Go around your group and ask each person to share any decision she feels ready to make. Working by yourself, note down any decision you want to make. If you haven't come to any conclusions or made any decisions, you don't have to fake one – just say or note down that you don't want to make any decisions yet.

Exercise 33   Voice exercise

Become aware how your voice vibrates in different parts of your body. Sit tall, legs crossed, spine lifting, back of your

neck long. (If you feel tired, lean against a wall, or alter-
natively, sit back to back, which gives you a lovely warm
feeling.)

Let your eyes close, and let your breathing slow down.
When you are settled, start to hum an 'mm' sound on the
breath out. After the initial feeling of strangeness you will
probably find that this is pleasant and soothing. Choose
any note, high or low, and choose any volume, loud or soft.
Your breaths will become long and steady. Notice how the
'mm' vibrates in your lips and forehead.

Without disturbing yourself, change to an 'oo' sound for
a few breaths, sing it high or low, loud or soft as you like,
on your out breaths. Notice how your head and upper chest
vibrate with the sound. Try out 'ah' and 'oh' sounds as well.
With an 'ah' sound you will feel the ribcage, throat and
skull vibrate and with an 'oh' sound you will feel hips,
ribcage and head all vibrate, and you may be able to feel the
sound in your arms and legs as well. After a few 'oh'
sounds, let your voice die away, and breathe gently for a
few moments until you feel like blinking your eyes open.
Chanting in this simple way can help you to extend the
range of potential of your voice.

Exercise 34   Colour meditation

Rest on the floor as for 'Deep relaxation', Exercise 12. Let
one person read these instructions slowly, pausing between
each sentence:

Choose your colour – stick to colours in the rainbow
spectrum and avoid blacks and browns. Pick the first colour
that comes into your head. Be aware of any associations
that this colour has for you.

Imagine this colour glowing in the centre of your body
just below your navel, and then imagine it spreading out
through your body. Let it spread through your chest and

hips, let it flood down your arms and legs, and flow through your neck into your head. Now let your colour shine out through your skin like a halo. Let the halo spread further and further until it fills the room. Pause.

Now feel the halo of your colour coming back in towards you until it is a small halo. Let the colour settle back in within your skin. Let it flow slowly back to the centre of your body, till it is a small glow at the centre of your body. On a breath out, finally breathe your colour away. When you feel like it, blink your eyes open and slowly sit up.

Share with the others in your group which colour you chose, how it felt to fill up with and radiate your colour, and anything else that seems relevant. If you are on your own, write these things down. It can be a harmonising experience, and you might like to think about what you needed and got from the colour you generated. Once you have done this a few times you can do it in just a few minutes if you are in the middle of a day where you feel particularly rattled, and it can help you to regain your equilibrium.

If you are doing these exercises as you read through, leave a week until you move on to the next chapter, but keep a note of impressions and dreams that strike you during the week.

CHAPTER 4

Assertiveness – finding our personal power

This chapter is about assertiveness. It is an important skill to practise during the first year after having a baby. Spending many hours a day with such a vulnerable person as a tiny baby somehow makes you feel more vulnerable too. Your concentration and involvement in the contained world of you and your baby may leave you very shaky when you have to arrange things, communicate, enquire and generally interact with the outside world.

Confidence ebbs away. Anyone from outside being brisk, uncooperative, or nasty, is shattering. If you worked outside the home before you had a baby you may wonder with astonishment how you ever managed to do your job, and feel certain you will never be able to do it again. Siobhan was editor of a newspaper women's page before her baby was born. She described how a few weeks after the baby's arrival an old colleague came to stay. While she worked with him she had not felt he was particularly brilliant, but during his visit she found herself constantly deferring to his views about journalism and having no confidence at all in her own ideas. She felt as though she wasn't really able to have professional opinions any more, and as though there was nothing to back her up. She was feeling a real loss suffered by many of us after

Advice from everyone

birth – a loss of identity, of personal authority, of a sense of self-worth.

You will also be the recipient of babycare advice from everyone: the woman in the chemist's, the paediatrician, your mother-in-law, your best friend, your worst enemy. Whether or not they have had any contact with a real baby in the last thirty years, or ever, will not stand in their way if they have something they want to say. The only time this flow dries up is if you ask for advice, at which point everyone goes vague and says 'I don't know, it's up to you, wait and see, give it another week', and so forth. You need assertiveness skills to fend off anything that feels like interference, and to press for clear information when you need it.

After having a baby you need to relearn the sense of grown-up confidence which allows you to ring up the plumber, and even more so the sense of grown-up con-

fidence which you need to call the plumber back and say the
thing he's mended is still leaking and you want him back at
once to repair it – not next Thursday fortnight at an
unspecified time so you have to stay in all day, but at once.

The basis of assertiveness is to learn a way of making
points, requests, refusals, and any other sort of statement,
without being aggressive, without cringing, and without
tying yourself in knots of awkwardness and apologies. The
method is clearly described in *A Woman in Your Own
Right*, by Ann Dickson, the woman who originated and
pioneered this approach. Try following her idea of identi-
fying four characters and 'types' of behaviour – Agnes the
aggressive woman, who hurts and gets hurt, lashing out
because of her own low self-esteem; Dulcie the doormat,
the victim and martyr; Ivy the mistress of atmospheres who
mediates her anger and frustration through manipulation
and innuendo; and Selma, the assertive woman, who
respects herself and others, asks clearly for what she wants
and needs in life, but is not devastated by refusal or
rejection. Notice how in different areas of your life you
behave now like one, now like another of these characters.
Practising assertiveness should help you spend more time in
the positive, assertive 'Selma' role, and less in the others.

Choose at least one exercise from each section, as in
previous chapters, to open your session, do some solid
work in the middle section, and close your session well.

Section one – exercises to begin the session

Exercise 35   How I compete . . .

One of the struggles we have when we try to share with
other women is finding that we are conditioned to compete
with one another. Our sincere intentions otherwise cannot

always prevent us from comparing ourselves − are we cleverer, thinner, sexier, more successful than the other women here? Competition can take strange forms. One can find oneself competing as for who is the most miserable or the most broke or the most disadvantaged. One may want to have the nastiest husband or the most acute health problems. The pain of all this competition is the pain of trying to share space where we may have learned as young girls and women that the only way to get any space was to compete for it. Trying to think clearly about ways in which you compete should give you some interesting, if uncomfortable, material to work on. If you are working on your own, set aside five minutes to make a list of the ways in which you compete, and give yourself time to read and think about them. Make notes or drawings of any examples you feel like exploring more fully, and note down any incidents or reasons you can see or remember which made you want to compete in your particular ways. Don't ignore examples which seem trivial − note them down; if they come into your mind they have something to say to you.

If you are in a group, have five minutes to think over and note down on a piece of paper ways in which you compete. Think about the different areas of your life: friends, families, motherhood, health, work outside the home, your creative life, your emotional life, dealings with strangers, and so on. Where and on what grounds do you compete? When you come into a group of women or meet another woman what do you feel competitive about?

Our groups found that our answers were wide-ranging: 'I compete about my income. I want to feel I'm well off . . .', 'I compete over qualifications and status. I need to feel ahead of the field there . . .', 'I compete about how sociable my baby is. I think it shows what a good social life I have and I want people to know that!' There were bits of 'negative' competition: 'I need people to think my life is difficult. I compete to be having the most complicated time emotionally', and 'I am so tired. I want to be the most tired. I don't want to admit that anybody else could be as tired as I am – so I compete on tiredness'. Also there was the unexpected: 'Fingernails. I take a lot of care of my fingernails and I keep them very long and I paint them. I get annoyed if anybody else has got fingernails longer than mine', the gruelling: 'It means an awful lot to me to be fit and I go jogging most days and feel competitive about being very fit', and the maternal: 'I feel competitive about being the best mother here'.

Go around your group and share your list. If you want to express other thoughts about what you've written – surprise, regret, desire for a change, or insight into why you compete in these areas – do so. Women need to develop an ability to be strong together, not to see each other's strengths as a threat. This exercise helps us to understand how hard that is, that we are not alone in feeling competitive.

Exercise 36   Learning to shout

You thought about the range of your voice in Exercise 33. How about its power? In a group you can only do this really if all the babies are resting and you can go into a different room from them – otherwise they will be frightened! Similarly, on your own, you need to get away from the baby so that you don't scare her.

Warm your voice up. Sit with your back supported against a wall or the front of an armchair or settee, or sit with a partner back to back, enjoying the warmth and support of each other's spines. Close your eyes. When you feel ready, on the breaths out, start to hum. Hum as quietly or loudly as you like – hum a single note or a string of different notes. Notice the hum vibrating in your lips and forehead. At first giggles and embarrassment may inhibit you, but soon you will be making strange music together. Listen as well as humming. It is a lovely sound. After some minutes begin to sing with your mouth open 'ah', 'oh' or 'ee' sounds, single notes or tunes. Open your throat. Let your ribcage and pelvis vibrate with the sound. After a few more minutes let the sound die away. Blink your eyes open and stand up, tearing yourself reluctantly away from the warmth of your partner's back. Choose a word or phrase you want to shout and shout together!

Shout each person's word or phrase three times. It helps to stretch your arms up or to punch the air as you shout, or to stamp your foot. If you're on your own shout what you want to. You may like to switch some music on loud to disguise your shouting from the neighbours! Shouting while driving the car is a good chance, or while some horrible noisy domestic appliance is switched on (hoover, spindryer, foodblender). In our groups we often wanted to shout 'Help!', 'No', 'Leave me alone', and 'Listen to me', amongst other things! Sometimes people just want to roar. Have a good roar. After you finish have a good shake all over and a good stretch. Notice how you feel compared with the way you felt before you shouted.

Exercise 37   If I got angry I would . . .

This exercise is a chance to speculate on what would happen if you began to let your anger out. I notice in myself a tendency to talk about being angry and to being intellectually angry, without letting myself feel the anger emotionally, and therefore, presumably, expressing it. I am far more likely to feel weepy or frustrated or bitter than to allow myself to touch that scary and raw emotion anger.

For group work – get into pairs and give each other four minutes to say sentences beginning 'If I got angry I would . . .'. Sit comfortably opposite one another. If you aren't the partner saying the sentences, don't say anything at all. Don't worry if there are quite long silences, it may take some time for your thoughts to form and come to the surface.

When you have both had your four minutes have another four minutes to talk together about what came up. Did the things you said have a link? Were they, for example, concerned with upsetting other people, or becoming physically violent, or being disliked, or your self-image being threatened? Share with each other your reactions.

Section two – exercises for the main part of the session

Exercise 38   Making a list

Working alone, or working in a group, this is a written exercise. Let your mind range around the various different circumstances of your life and the people you have to deal with. Think about how you deal with strangers, partners, people in authority, relatives, salespeople, colleagues. Now try to make a list of situations where you would like, or would have liked, to have been more assertive. Aim for at least five items on your list – although sometimes you might feel impelled to write down twenty or thirty! Try to keep your list based mainly in the present but include recurring predicaments, and anything that comes vividly into your mind from a long time ago. One woman included a situation from seventeen years ago in her list! It was worth working on because it was still relevant to her daily life. Don't assume that minor points are too trivial to write down. If it matters to you it's important and often, when you look at it, turns out to be part of a large and important pattern. Give yourself ten quiet minutes to make your list.

Now follow Ann Dickson's advice in *A Woman in Your Own Right* and write beside each point the attitude you presently have to the situation: aggressive, passive, or manipulative. She also suggests numbering the points on your list in order of difficulty, and being careful, in your 'real' life, to begin by working on the easier issues, where you may have some success which will build your confidence, and help you move on to the trickier issues in a stronger frame of mind.

This is a private list and you need not show it to anybody else. However, you might like to keep your list, even if you are either working alone and keeping a book, or keeping a book as a back-up for your group work. It can be interesting to look back in a few months and see which situations you have been able to act on and which are still stuck. The truly heartening thing is that some things which have in the past felt stuck like concrete can be changed.

Exercise 39 *Assertiveness practice*

Ann Dickson formulates these three useful guidelines for good assertiveness practice:

1 decide what you want to say;
2 say it direct, without padding, to the person concerned; and
3 stick to it, repeating it if necessary, and avoid getting hooked.

Several women found it useful to copy these points out and sellotape them up next to the telephone! You also need to learn them clearly so that you can remember them in a face to face conversation.

Taking the points one by one: the first point sounds

terribly obvious – but is it? Most situations that make you feel tense also inhibit the power of articulate speech and thought. You may find yourself spluttering instead. It's useful to spend some time saying to yourself: 'If I could really say what I wanted to, what would it be?', and to practise saying whatever it is in your group, even if it's something which at this stage you very much doubt you could say in 'real' life.

Secondly, when you have worked out what you want to say, you should, when you feel ready to, try saying it. Don't pad it out and obscure it with the blather that most of us produce by the yard when trying to say something difficult – 'I hope you won't mind me saying this', 'I'm awfully sorry to interrupt you . . .', 'Would it possibly be OK if . . .' are phrases you can do without. They make what you are saying less clear and less powerful.

You should say your assertive point to the person concerned, and not to their best friend, auntie or budgerigar in the hope that it will be passed on! It's so easy to say to person (a) that person (b) is bugging you. It's hard to find a clear and constructive way of saying it to person (b). Hard, but often a lot more worthwhile. Sticking to it, the final point, means practising calmly repeating your point, and not getting dragged into irrelevant arguments, or getting wound up, or harassed.

Try out assertive responses yourself in this exercise. If you are in a group get into groups of three. If you are alone, try out your assertive responses first in writing, then out loud. Take five minutes to think about three situations you would like to work on. Let one of these be a situation in which you want to make a clear request, one a situation where you would like to make a clear refusal, and one a more general predicament.

Make a note of what you want to say – or if you can't get clear about that, ask for suggestions from your group until you have clarified it, then write it down. Your task is, one person at a time, to explain briefly the background to your situation, and to make your assertive statement, with eye contact, to each of the other people in your group: 'Why are you always late home?', 'I would like some more demonstrative affection', 'No thank you, I won't come to the coffee morning', 'I want to stop breastfeeding', 'I want an appointment to see the doctor', 'I would like to talk about sharing the housework', 'No thank you, we've decided to spend Christmas at home', 'Please sit down for a moment and listen to what I have to say', 'I've decided not to eat fattening cakes for a while', 'No thank you, I don't want a drink'. These are some of the things which cropped up in our group.

If it's something you've needed to say for a long time, the relief of finally saying it can make you burst into tears, or burst out laughing! After you have all had a go of saying your sentences, practise sticking to them. Say the sentence again to each person in your group and let her argue with you. Show that you have heard what she says, but return calmly to your original statement. Do not get pulled into an argument, however difficult it is not to:

'I understand that you feel you drive better when you're drunk, but I'd still like to drive home tonight';

'It's lovely of you to bake a cake, but I've decided not to eat fattening cakes for a while';

'I realise you're disappointed, but we have decided to spend Christmas at home';

'I know you're under a lot of pressure at work, but I would still like some more affection';

'I'm sure the surgery is busy, but I want an appointment to see a doctor today';

'I know you feel strongly that breastfeeding is best, but I still want to stop doing it';

'Yes, it is a great party, but I don't want a drink'.

Susan felt compromised by the assumptions people made about her beliefs. Because she is clearly a feminist, progress-ive woman, the people around her assumed that she was pro-abortion, and talked casually about a mutual friend's choice of termination of pregnancy in a way that upset her. She acted this out with a partner and came to a good resolution of the difficulty:

Partner: 'Well, Vera got her abortion fixed up, so that's fine isn't it, a great relief all round.'

Susan: 'Actually, I want to say that I don't agree with abortion and it upsets me very much to hear you talk like that.'

Partner: 'But you're a feminist aren't you? And you want what's best for Vera don't you? I thought you were all for freedom of choice for women.'

Susan: 'I am a feminist, yes, but I still don't agree with abortion.'

Partner: 'Well, I never expected to hear you being so stuffy.'

Susan: 'I don't think I'm stuffy, I just don't agree with abortion.'

Partner: 'What about if the baby's handicapped? What about rape victims? Are you sure you've really thought about it properly?'

Susan: 'I don't want to go into all that now. I just want to tell you that I feel very upset that everyone just assumes I'm in favour of it. I'm not.'

Partner (shrugs): 'Well, you're entitled to your point of view I suppose.'

Susan: 'Thank you. And you're entitled to yours.'

If you are working alone, try to imagine what arguments may be raised, and how you can acknowledge the points without being steamrollered by them. The elation that you feel when you first use this technique effectively is well worth the nervousness that you feel when you first try it out.

Exercise 40   Towards self-defence

No woman today, young or old, pregnant, lactating, or with small children, can count herself immune to the risk of physical attack. In our society where men's fantasies are encouraged by the pornographic industry to link sex with sadism and power, it seems that no-one is innocent enough, vulnerable enough, helpless enough, to be safe from attack. There is a huge question of what is to be done to change the way boys and men in this society develop their sexual identity and sense of physical strength. But for women now, our daughters, our friends, our mothers, ourselves, the question is how to be more safe with things as they are. We can follow obvious safety guidelines: not walking in the dark alone, not hitching lifts or accepting lifts from strangers, looking in our own cars before we get in to check no-one is hiding. We can avoid publicising our addresses and telephone numbers, and check the identity of anyone who comes into our homes to do work or repairs. It is unjust that we, who do not do the harm, have our lives curbed and limited in this way.

All women should consider seriously taking some sort of training in self-defence. We must also remember that no amount of expertise in self-defence can make us perfectly safe, and we have to continue to observe the safety guidelines as well. Kaleghl Quinn's book *Stand Your Ground* would be a useful investment for any woman beginning to think about learning self-defence.

For this exercise in your group, simply begin to feel what it might be like to punch and kick effectively, and learn one defensive manoeuvre to help you in the case of a strangle attack.

PUNCHING
Stand with your feet hip-distance apart. Bend your knees a little and 'sit down'. Curl your hands into fists with your thumbs on the outside and, bending your elbows, settle your fists by your waist. To punch with the right hand, unbend your arm slowly forwards, with your fist palm up, until it is nearly straight. At the last moment twist the wrist round and punch with the fist palm downwards. Pull your fist back into your waist. Imagine the contact is with the knuckle of your index and third finger. Making sure knees are still bent, punch with the left hand, in the same way. Then draw your left hand back to your waist. Practise punching a few more times, then practise punching once with each step, using the same arm as the foot that makes the step. As your feeling of power increases, swing your shoulder into the punch as well. Notice how it feels. At first it may well feel uncoordinated and silly, but you will gradually build up a feeling of power. It may help to shout with each punch.

KICKING
Stand with left foot forward, right foot back. Bend your knees. Guard your face with your hands in a loose, relaxed guard. Transferring your weight to your left foot, raise the right leg, knee bent. Kick out by straightening your right leg. Pull your toes back so that the ball of the foot would be the point of contact. Keep your left leg slightly bent. Draw the right leg back by bending at the knee again, then bringing the foot down behind the left foot, and transfer the weight evenly to both feet.

Practise your kick a few times in slow motion: then try it

out fast, snapping back the knee as soon as the kick is made, so that you cannot be caught by the foot. Practise equally with the left and the right leg, and try kicking as you walk forwards. Shout with each kick if it helps.

Practising kicking may have given you some information about the way you dress – can you move freely enough? Consider in your own mind whether anything about your style of dress may make you more vulnerable. Can you run well in the style of shoes you prefer? Are your legs restricted by your skirt or trousers? Are your earrings the kind that would pull out if someone pulled them, or could you be dragged by them? Does the hairstyle you prefer restrict your vision a great deal?

Do not practise punching or kicking for more than five minutes each this first time. They are such unfamiliar movements for most women that you will get very stiff afterwards if you do.

THROAT ATTACK
When you try this BE EXTREMELY CAREFUL, or you are going to hurt one another. The formality and ritual of a martial arts class is there to remind class members at all times to take care of one another. Take care of each other now. This manoeuvre may help you in the case of being attacked by a front stranglehold. This is a very dangerous attack as pressure on the throat and neck can cause you to black out within minutes, if not seconds.

Draw your chin in to protect your neck and the throat as much as you can. Now step your left foot back and with your right hand reach up to your attacker's throat. Using thumb and two fingers in a pincer action, attack his Adam's apple, imagining you are trying to make thumb and fingers meet round the back of the Adam's apple. When you practise the manoeuvre, do *not* pinch the Adam's apple, you will cause your partner great pain and discomfort.

Practise steadying yourself on the back foot and getting your hand to the correct position.

If you use this defence it will cause your attacker to cough, choke and his eyes to stream. You use this short respite to run away.

Never use this defence in fun or rough and tumble, but remember it if you are ever in the dangerous position of being attacked by a stranglehold.

DISCUSSION

These three physical activities can only give you a small taste of self-defence training. Proper martial arts training costs time and money – as do women's self-defence courses – but are something that, sadly, all women should seriously consider these days.

In your group, and, equally, on your own, see if you feel ready to make any decisions relating to your own ability to look after yourself physically, your own self-defence. You might decide to make enquiries about martial arts classes, or self-defence classes, to adjust your dress or behaviour in some way. Anything we can do to stay fit and healthy increases our capability of looking after ourselves. Any time we are able to choose not to be out drunk or stoned, not to be so choked up with cigarettes that we can't run, not to be wrapped in clothes or shoes that trip us, or jewellery that can be used to pull us by or hurt us with, we are working on our own good self-defence.

Exercise 41   Yes and no

The key to this exercise is body language. It is a simple exercise on saying 'No' and saying 'Yes' with appropriate body language. How often do you say 'No' with an uncertain smile or 'Yes' with an ill-disguised scowl, meanwhile falling off the edge of the table you are sitting perched on, or breaking the necklace you are fiddling with so that a million tiny beads cascade across the floor? If we can say what we mean, and back it up with appropriate body language, we really do become powerful.

In your group, all stand up and wander around the room in a random way, weaving in and out amongst each other. Do not trudge round the room together in a circle. After a while, as the fancy takes you, touch someone on the shoulder as they pass. That person must then turn and face you, balance her weight equally on both feet. She must look you in the eyes, breathe out, drop her shoulders, and say 'No'. Then move on again. In a few minutes you have lots of small experiences of hearing a clear 'No' and lots of experiences of saying a clear 'No'. Take heed of any tendency to a ghastly grin or rigid shoulders, or your gaze shifting to the floor or to over your friend's left shoulder into the middle distance. After a few minutes, stop and change to 'Yes'. When touched on the shoulder, turn to the person who did it, look her in the eye, and say 'Yes'. Notice what it's like to say 'Yes', with a smile and maybe a hug, and what it's like to receive a clear 'Yes'. After a few minutes stop and get into pairs. Sit down! Spend five or ten minutes chatting about how it felt to give and receive clear 'yeses' and 'nos' and also about times recently where you have given or received mixed up 'yeses' or 'nos'.

People often express concern that practising assertiveness will lose them friends and make a rude or aggressive impression on people. My experience is in fact the opposite – that friendships, partnerships, and business relationships are enhanced by an ability to say a clear 'No' and a clear 'Yes'. You will be more valued, not less, because people will feel that they know where they are with you. It is far more painful on both sides to give a muddled message which seems to read either 'Yes, but I don't really want to', or 'No, but I wish I could'.

You can give an assertive 'No' with an assertive explanatory statement: 'No, I won't come out for a drink tonight. I don't want to be tired out tomorrow'; 'No, I won't join in with that project. My workload is up to capacity already.' Also remember that you don't have to explain or justify a 'No' unless you want to. You might want to share the reasons for your refusal but you are not obliged to.

You may want to follow an assertive 'No' with an assertive protest: 'No, I won't tell lies on your behalf on the phone, and I don't want to be asked to tell lies on the phone again'; 'No I won't "just" type this letter – it's not part of my job'; 'No, I won't come on that picket'; 'No, I'm not going to spend Xmas at your mother's'.

One further hint about saying a good clear 'No' is to make a quick getaway after it. Most of us feel a temptation to prolong the conversation, saying things like 'Are you sure that's OK?' or 'Will you be able to manage?' or 'Will you be alright?' Try to resist it. Either move onto a new subject or close the conversation.

Last year I was due to lead an assertiveness course for professional women. The proofs of the brochure appeared with an illustration of a man kneeling at a woman's feet, kissing the hem of her skirt! I strode into the office and said that I would not lead the group if the illustration was not withdrawn. A furore ensued while everyone said it was too late, it had all gone to press, what was the problem, it was just a joke, and so on, and so forth. I said fine, but I won't lead the course. They said alright, alright, we'll do our best to stop it.

The next day I rang the office to find out what had happened, and they had successfully removed the illustration, so I was prepared to go ahead as agreed with the group. Then a wave of apologies came into my mind. It was almost impossible not to say thank you, thank you, I'm sorry to be a nuisance, I know how busy you are, it must have really messed up your day yesterday, we feminists have these funny little ways but we're not too bad underneath it all – and similar rubbish. I did resist it, but only just. I was rescued by remembering the rule that if you've got a clear message across, don't stick around afterwards fudging it all again.

Section three – exercise to close the session

Exercise 42   Finding your centre

Sit cross-legged, if you are tired resting your back against the wall or the front of a settee or armchair. If you are working in a group, let one person read the instructions out slowly, with pauses between the sentences. On your own read the instructions through a few times, until you are familiar with them, then close your eyes and do the exercise. Lift your spine and sit well up out of your hips. Relax your shoulders. Feel the back of your neck is long. Breathe a little more deeply and a little more slowly than usual.

Now get in touch with the quiet centre of yourself. Find the place where strength, love, and intuition come from, your centre of gravity, your quiet centre. If nothing comes immediately, don't worry. Just wait a little longer. (Short pause.) If any image or picture, or colour or sound comes into your mind, hold it there gently. At this moment it illustrates your centre. Let your breath flow in and out of your body without interfering with it at all. Stay in touch with your quiet centre. Pause. Your quiet centre is there inside you all the time. All that any of us needs is to be able to get in contact with it when we need to.

Now slowly bring your awareness back into the room.

Become aware of where you are – of the people around you, and the room around you. Take some deeper breaths and sigh them out. Now blink your eyes open and let them get used to the light. This is the end of the exercise. It leaves people quiet and subdued, but they may like to share quietly what they felt. A woman on her own may like to write down or make drawings of what she felt or perceived as her quiet centre. Think of it as a place you can quickly visit, or have a glimpse of, when you are under pressure. It is the place where strength and energy come from and it is therefore as important to do this kind of work as it is to do any of the dynamic or verbal exercises.

CHAPTER 5

More Babies? – thinking about more children, or no more children

Hardly has your newborn baby been tucked into his perspex crib before the questions about the next one start. If you had a lovely birth you may think to yourself 'Oh, I can't wait to do that again'. If you had a painful or difficult birth, of course, your emotions might be quite the reverse.

People assume on the whole that nobody wants an only child, and that nobody wants children of all one sex. Advice flows freely about 'having another before too long' and about exactly how long the ideal gap is between children. If you already have several children you may hear comments like 'Oh, you've got your girl (or boy) at last then', 'Oh, you'll be coming back in for the chop (sterilisation) soon then?' or 'Sending your old man for the chop (vasectomy) soon?' It's yet another example of how one's private thoughts and feelings are open for free-for-all assumption and discussion during pregnancy and birth.

Choices we make may not be on the bases those around us assume. We may want to say 'I haven't decided yet'. As well as external pressures, there are internal muddles. Many of us are torn between a desire for children and a fear of life cooped up in a house with small babies. This chapter explains how we tried in our groups to think about whether we want more children, or no more children. We did not try to make rigid plans. We tried to notice what the pressures are from within and without towards having more babies, and we tried to get clear about our own present points of view. Working alone these exercises are useful too: read through them and see what they bring to mind, and work through those that are suitable for doing alone.

Section one – exercises to begin the session

Exercise 43   Your pregnant self

Can you remember what it was like to be pregnant? Are you sure? It's amazing how quickly it can slip away. Concentrate on some specific moments and see if you can get in touch with them again. If you're working alone get your book out and some colours, felt tips, or crayons. Now think about the moment you knew for certain you were pregnant. How did it happen? Did you do a test at home and run into the bathroom to see if the test had changed colour or formed a ring? What was it like when you saw it was positive? Did you shout, sing, smile, burst into tears, sit down with a thud? Did you run to the telephone or hug your secret to you? Was it a shock or a disaster? Were you appalled? Perhaps you knew because of a moment of sudden nausea or giddiness, so different from your ordinary self that you knew you must have conceived. Where were you when it happened? What was going on around you?

Write in your book about the very moment you knew you were pregnant. Write about where you were, what you were doing, how you felt. Make a picture of yourself at that moment, or if you prefer, make a design or pattern which illustrates your feelings at that moment. Do both if you like.

If you are working in a group, get into pairs and have five minutes each to speak about the moment when you discovered you were pregnant, the circumstances, and your feelings at the time. Now concentrate on a time about halfway through the pregnancy. Can you remember how things were going at about twenty weeks, or four and a half months into the pregnancy? How were you feeling? How were you spending your days? Was your baby moving about and kicking you a lot? Did you look and feel very pregnant? Were people treating you differently from usual?

If you are working by yourself write about this midway point of the pregnancy. Remember what you enjoyed and what you hated, and how that very particular time was. Make a drawing – maybe of yourself at twenty weeks pregnant, or of anything else that symbolises that time for you. In a group, swop partners, and have five minutes each to talk about the mid-point of your pregnancy.

Now move on to eight and a half months into the pregnancy, or a week or two before delivery. Just before your baby was ready to be born, what was life like for you? What were you spending your time doing? What was it like physically carrying an almost-ready baby around inside you? What kind of things did you think about? Write and draw about it, or, in a group, change partners once more and have five minutes each to talk about the last few days of your pregnancy.

Exercise 44   Your new-mother self

Work in the same way on the early days of motherhood. Focus on a time about three weeks after your baby was born. Conjure it up again. Where were you? Who was around you? How did you spend your days? How were you feeling? Write about that time early in your baby's life, and make some pictures – perhaps one of yourself and your baby, and one of your general moods at the time. You can do this by yourself, or if you are in a group you can spend ten or fifteen minutes doing writing or drawing, and then get into twos to share what you have written and drawn with each other.

Section two – exercises for the main part of the session

Exercise 45   More children?

Take ten or fifteen minutes to write about these five questions:

1   Imagine your household and set-up in two years time. Who do you expect to be living with you? How do you envisage spending your days? What will you be putting your energy into? Do you see any more children being part of your life in two years time?

2   Imagine your household and set-up in five years time. Who would you expect to be living with you in five years time? How do you envisage spending your days? What will you be putting your energies into? Do you see any more children being part of your life in five years time?

3   In another pregnancy what would you hope to do the same as you did this time? What would you hope to do differently?

4   During another delivery what would you hope to do the same as you did this time? What would you hope to do differently?

5   During the first six weeks of your baby's life what would you hope to do in the same way as you did this time? What would you hope to do differently?

Consider each question slowly and carefully, and write everything down that comes into your mind. If you are working alone take time to read it all through afterwards and notice how focusing on particular dates and moments can help you to crystallise your thoughts. If you are in a group, get together in small groups of threes or fours and share what you wrote, and your reactions to it.

One woman with a new baby and a toddler spoke of her feelings about having more children being coloured by the fact that she was approaching her 'thousandth broken night'! Many women notice that they do not visualise another baby in two years, but do imagine at least one more at the five-year landmark. This depends on the circumstances in which you are living and bringing up your child: whether you are alone or with a partner and how changeable the future looks.

One may feel a clear determination to handle the pregnancy, the birth, or the first few weeks of a baby's life quite differently. Women often talk about taking more exercise and eating less during their next pregnancy, about avoiding being bullied by GPs, consultants or midwives. On the positive side women may talk of making sure they do plenty of swimming again, of getting back in touch with a midwife or doctor who made them feel respected and well-cared-for again, of experiencing once more the joy of having a living being kicking around inside them. The period shortly after the birth is often described as rather a lurid time: 'I didn't know what had hit me', 'I walked around like a zombie', 'I cried every day' – and these were all women who adore their babies and were, on the surface of it, coping very well and 'quite happy'. Considering how the post-natal period might be differently handled brings a strong response: 'I'm *determined* not to be so isolated next time. I shall really plan ahead and make sure I see plenty of people from the word go'; 'I'm not going to leap up so bloody fast this time.

I'm going to spend plenty of time resting. I was so proud of myself being up and about after a week this time, but I regretted it later. Once I was up and dressed I definitely got less help than I would have done if I'd stayed in bed in my pyjamas for longer'; 'I'm going to start exercising sooner. After a couple of months had gone by and I'd done nothing, it hardly seemed worth starting any more'; 'I'm looking forward to doing it all again just with some sense that I know what I'm doing. I mean the first time it's just unknown territory, isn't it?'

That last remark was echoed over and over again – a feeling that for most of us, growing up as a girl in society today does not equip you with enough shared experiences of pregnancy, birth and new babies to help you cope when you have your own baby. The experience of previous terminations of pregnancy may appear during this session. It may be a time when women want to speak about pregnancies that they did not continue up to full term, and the mixed emotions which inevitably follow.

Other women in the group may have experienced miscarriage or stillbirth. They may want to share their experiences too. It may be hard for women who have lost babies through miscarriage or stillbirth to speak with women who have chosen to end a pregnancy, and vice versa. All we can do is to try not to judge one another, to try to make space for each other to share feelings. Since contact with this baby inevitably puts us in mind of contact with any other babies or potential babies in our lives, it is useful to be aware that these topics may come up.

Exercise 46   *The art of contraception*

How amazing it is that the human race has the technology to put people on the moon, but not to produce an acceptable, non-intrusive, non-dangerous form of contraception.

If you do not want to conceive again very quickly, and you are in a heterosexual partnership, you are going to have to do something about contraception. Breastfeeding may suppress your fertility, but the degree of suppression varies from woman to woman and cannot be relied upon to guarantee contraception. If you are in a group, have a brainstorm together about contraception, a discussion where you pool ideas and experiences. Sadly there is likely to be a spate of horror stories and gruesome anecdotes.

One woman put it glumly and succinctly: 'I'm back to pill-hopping'. Another described her GP fitting her with a diaphragm. She returned to have it checked after a few weeks and he decided it was the wrong size. 'Good thing you came back,' he remarked, 'it would have been bad for my reputation if you'd got pregnant again, wouldn't it?'

For Olivia, having a diaphragm fitted was humiliating: 'I expressed a desire to use a diaphragm and was fitted for one only four weeks after delivery. They said they hadn't got one big enough and various people stood around at the end of the bed and joked about having to order me a specially big one, which they did. I had to go back the next week to collect it and heard more of the same stuff about how they'd never had to issue one as big as that, and so forth. I felt devastated. I really felt I was ruined internally. It was literally years before I understood that they had fitted the thing too soon after the delivery and I was still a bit stretched from the birth. I never used it. I went to another clinic and went on the pill. I worried about needing this enormous diaphragm for a long time afterwards.'

No doubt there will be IUD stories too, often along the lines of bleeding after insertion ('I bled so much it felt like the end of the world') and heavy cramping and bleeding during subsequent periods. Also there is a lingering question to which it is hard to get a straight answer – Does it work by early abortion? 'It's a bit of a mystery,' was the answer one woman got from her GP. Many women on the pill feel that they're never sure whether their moods are their own, and nagging doubts about other side-effects will sometimes frighten them.

Sheaths and diaphragms are enjoying renewed popularity because of their protective effects. A diaphragm seems to have a protective effect on the cervix, and the sheath of course is protective in terms of the AIDS virus and other venereal diseases, as well as protective of the cervix. They both have disadvantages in terms of spontaneity: 'We've had this baby because we were supposed to be using sheaths. We got carried away. I don't know if I've got any faith in us using them now'; and the dreaded creams and jellies: 'That spermicide is not supposed to be something you can be allergic to, but my boyfriend says it makes him stinging and sore'; 'I have to stage manage it to get some KY jelly in while my husband's in the loo if I think we're going to end up making love – because I think he thinks I don't get as turned on as I used to, but I think it's just the sheaths. Mad isn't it?' However, the barrier methods don't mess up your hormones or make you feel as though your body is being radically messed about with.

If you can't stand any more of the contraceptive drugs or software, you could try the 'natural' approach. If you are prepared to make three observations each day – your temperature, your cervical position and state (open or closed), and your mucus, you can tell accurately when you are ovulating. Each of these observations on its own is rather risky, but plotting the three on the chart together gives you a triple check, and seems to be pretty reliable. It leaves you with about ten days per month where you should not have intercourse. This might give you an incentive and an opportunity to find other ways of making love which might be marvellously liberating for your partnership. If, on the other hand, ten days without intercourse every month seems far too much, you could use a barrier method (sheath or diaphragm) during the ten days. The correct way to make the three crucial observations is explained in detail in *Natural Fertility Awareness* by John and Farida Davidson. It is quite satisfying to feel that you are in touch with your cycle, and, of course, if and when you want to conceive again, the knowledge you have of when you ovulate will help you to conceive.

At the other extreme there is the option of sterilisation by surgery. You can arrange for your fallopian tubes to be cut or tied so that no more eggs can pass from your ovaries to your womb and you cannot become pregnant. It is difficult to reverse this process surgically so it must be regarded as permanent. Mother Nature, however, is very determined and occasionally (one in five or six hundred cases) the tubes recanalise by themselves. Thus, at your interview with your consultant you may be told on the one hand that there is no going back on this operation, but that on the other hand there is a small failure rate.

It is a radical step, and you need to spend plenty of time thinking it over before you take it. For some women it is a pleasing way of being rid, once and for all, of the harassment of contraception. Others, however, regret it bitterly. Avril spoke of her sterilisation, carried out shortly after the birth of her fourth baby: 'I *knew* when they brought me the forms to sign, that I was doing the wrong thing. I knew it but I couldn't say anything. I signed the forms and they went ahead, and it was a ghastly mistake.' Many women go on the waiting list for the operation, only to find that when their date finally comes they cannot face going through with it.

It might be worth making a pause between the birth of a baby and a sterilisation operation. The shock of life with a tiny baby might colour your decision to an extent that you would later want to modify. However, at the moment the waiting lists are so long that you could go on the list and still have several months to spare for your deliberations!

All the awful complications and drawbacks with contraception should not of course blind us to the fact that we are really only the first and second generations of women who have had any other choices than celibacy or perpetual pregnancy, lactation, miscarriage or birth. In your group discussion, as well as moans and groans, you will also hear about satisfactory compromises and solutions to the contraceptive question, and these may give you new ideas and information.

Exercise 47   *Other people's views*

It may be that there are some people in your life who strongly want you to have more children, and others who strongly wish you to have no more children. If you are working alone divide a page of your book into two columns. On one side write about those people who you feel would like you to have more babies. On the other write about anyone who wants you to stop now with the number of children you already have. If you are in a group write for five minutes in your two columns, then go around the group sharing the contents of your lists.

Many women speak of their mother's or their partner's mother's strong desire for more grandchildren. Existing children may ask for brothers and sisters, partners may long for more babies. One woman was taken aback when her mother said to her 'Don't have any more children, will you, you're like me, not maternal at all' – quite a bundle of messages! Sometimes a partner, feeling constricted and pressurised by parenthood, will express strong disfavour towards more children. This can feel like a rejection of your present baby – and many women experience that by extension as a rejection of themselves, of 'their department' of the family's life. Whatever material you discover, it is useful to notice if there is pressure to have, or avoid having, more children, and if so where it comes from.

Exercise 48   New and good

Go around your group and share one new, good thing you will be doing next week, however tiny, or however momentous: 'Start knitting a new sweater', 'Have a big meal in a nice restaurant', 'See or contact a friend I haven't seen for a long time', 'Doing the washing so it's not piling up', 'Dying my hair a different colour', 'Putting some fresh flowers in my room', 'Having an early night', 'Buy some crayons'.

Exercise 49   Candle gazing

Clear a space on the floor. Collect any favourite flowers, shells, crystals, or stones. Arrange them around a candle set

Candle gazing

safely on a saucer or in a candlestick. Draw the curtains, and switch off any electric lights.

Light the candle, and settle yourself in a comfortable sitting position. Look at your lovely flowers and shells, bathed in the candle's glow. Now take your gaze to the flame. Look steadily at the candle flame. Let your breathing be slow and steady and feel yourself becoming peaceful as you focus on the flame.

After a while close your eyes and see the flame in your mind's eye. After a few more minutes open your eyes and gaze at the flame again. Close and open your eyes at intervals a few more times, becoming more and more centred on the source of light. Finally blow the candle out and lie down for a few minutes deep relaxation.

CHAPTER 6

Tragedies and Challenges – the experience of stillbirth, and the challenge of caring for a handicapped child

The vast majority of us are lucky enough to have healthy, live babies. Our problems in the post-natal years are to do with re-organising our energies, expectations, and futures. Hard though it is to cope with the early years we look forward to our children growing towards, at the best, a happy independence.

Things are different if your baby dies at or around the time of birth, and different again if your baby is born with a physical or mental handicap. You begin your post-natal year in the midst of a tragedy or a very stiff challenge. None of this gets you out of the exhaustion and struggle of physical recovery, and makes your work on trying to see the future both poignant and difficult. Wendy shares here the experience of the birth of baby Kate:

It is hard for me to say how I am feeling now, I feel I am living in a false world most of the time because, although I have my daughter, Kate, home now and am continuing as in a normal situation, each day I am grateful for because I know I could lose her any day.

The day Kate was due Mr Boyd told me he thought she was a breech baby, not cephalic[1] as everyone had told me. I had a scan done to confirm this and an x-ray to see if my pelvis was big enough to deliver her normally. I was very upset as I knew that my chances of a normal birth were lessened and I was told I might need a Caesarean (now all that seems so irrelevant). As she was a week overdue I had time to adjust to the idea as much as I could, but where I had been confident and looking forward to it I was now apprehensive.

My labour started on Thursday evening (4 April) and started to become regular in the night and Mike and I became quite excited and did not get much sleep. In the morning I telephoned the hospital and got ready to go in, but outside the hospital the pains stopped and Mike practically had to force me in! I was glad that on examination I was 3 cms dilated and had not wasted their time but I still did not get the contractions so Mike went off to get some lunch. When he arrived back in the ward he was really surprised as the examination had got things moving very quickly and strongly! I was moving about trying to get comfortable but did not really succeed, whether this was due to the change in circumstances and that the doctors wanted me to have an epidural, I don't know. I asked them to leave me as long as possible knowing I would have the epidural because of the breech position and perhaps the need to operate. I was glad that I had reached 8 cms on my own, without help, and quite quickly from the 3 cms (I am glad now I had at least had something of the labour) but from then on there was not much to be happy about. I know I should have controlled my fear of having an epidural and

[1] A 'cephalic' baby is lying in the womb head downwards, ready to be born head first. A breech baby is curled up in the womb head up, and will be born bottom or feet first. This may complicate the delivery.

I did try but I could not help feeling frightened. By this time the contractions were difficult to cope with in the position needed to do the epidural and I found it extremely hard to relax. The epidural did not work, it only made me numb everywhere else except the area of pain deep in the pubic area. This only confirmed my fear and the anaesthetist had to do the whole thing again, stopping at each contraction which was becoming unbearable. I could not help yelling as that was about all I could move with all the messing about on my back.

At last he had finished and the pains were lessened until I felt completely numb, it was an awful feeling, so heavy and helpless, but at least I began to feel less exhausted. My labour slowed right down then and it was nearly 9.00 p.m. on Friday when they decided I had reached 10 cms but nothing was happening. We waited and waited but the monitors showed no sign and I often needed oxygen as the baby's heart beat fell low. I just wanted to get it all over with, it had gone on so long now and I was so uncomfortable getting pressure sores from staying still. The doctor decided I should try and push anyway (they knew I wanted a normal birth) about 11.30 p.m. and I knew they only gave me till 12.30 a.m. I tried for about fifty minutes, I really wanted this baby now and I was waiting for them to tell me they could see something but I knew they were not expecting anything because they often missed the contractions on the monitor to tell me when to push. My poor Mike was going through as much and he was really trying to help me push and kept telling me he could see my efforts although I hardly felt anything happening.

My time was eventually up and I was resigned to the Caesarean which I said I would have while under epidural so I could see my baby. They did not want Mike to be there. I think now they knew something would be wrong,

Mike thought this too but gladly did not say so to me, at that time you still do not believe anything terrible could happen to you.

I found the Caesarean quite uncomfortable and painful at times and the doctors told me I could have a general anaesthetic but I only wanted my baby and would bear it. I started to cry when they said they had her legs, at last I had a baby. I felt so happy, I felt her being pulled out, a really strange feeling, and she was handed over to paediatricians. I tried to be patient knowing they needed to clear her nose and throat but time started to pass and I knew something was wrong. I began to get hysterical because the nurses were telling me they thought she was alright but I still had not seen her. The doctor asked if I wanted something for the pain as I could feel them sewing me up but suddenly I felt no pain and my body went limp and I didn't care any more about anything. I could have died at that moment knowing my baby had something wrong. I was given a hypnotic drug and was asleep for about an hour.

When I came round I was still crying, Mike looking shattered above me and faces all around. Now I did not want to see my baby, did not want to see what I had done to her. I felt so guilty. I'll never be able to forget this awful time. A time we both wanted to be our happiest turned out the worst night we had ever been through. Poor Mike had been in a waiting-room all the time I was in theatre and was eventually told by a rather cool doctor that 'You have a baby girl, but she is seriously deformed.' He felt he could collapse at that moment but knew he had to come and see me. It took some time for everyone to persuade me to see my child, I was so absolutely shattered. My whole body had emotionally been torn apart and I hope I never feel anything so devastating again. I remember the nurse crying as well trying to tell me how much my child needed me, inside I knew I had to see her but I was so frightened, but I knew I had Mike by me all the time as I was wheeled to the special care unit.

When I was handed this small bundle I felt quite different. I laughed and cried, how could I have said I did not want to see her, she was so small and so innocent. I knew I felt love for her then. I was not able to see her body properly as the nurses were concerned with keeping her warm and getting her in an incubator so it was not till late in the afternoon that we saw her again. I was taken up to the ward around 5 a.m. Saturday morning feeling an absolute wreck.

I was not able to hold her until Sunday when she could come out of the incubator and breathe properly. Her poor body was a shock to us, she was unable to move apart from her hands and face, but I started to care for her and found it easier to cope with. I felt so disappointed that I had not held her when she was born and been able to breastfeed her. I tried several times while in hospital but she was not strong enough and got so upset we had to stop, I cannot help feeling I've been deprived of something special. I expressed milk for a month but did not have much due to all the upsets but I had to do this for my own peace of mind.

That week in hospital was awful, I've never cried so much in my life, sometimes I felt I could rip the room apart and could not go on. I don't know where I got strength from and I managed to continue. I also developed an infection in the wound which did not help matters at all.

We accepted our daughter as she was, we tried to think only from day to day but could not help thinking of our future, we tried to plan how we could cope with her and make her life worthwhile. Then after several tests and a muscle biopsy from her leg, the doctors told us they thought she had a muscle disease, spinal muscular atrophy, and would only have months to live. The first week of Kate's life was terrible for her, she had to go through so many tests, some quite painful for her, she began to get upset (although she could not cry properly) each time she was handled and started to go blue several times a day.

I visited her every day and when she was nearly five weeks old we took her home. She had developed a cold and was very weak. She already had a lot of problems with her respiratory system and we did not think she had long to live. I could not bear the thought of leaving her in hospital and someone telephoning me to tell me she had gone. She needed a lot of looking after with frequent sucking out to clear her nose and throat and she only took small amounts of milk with difficulty.

Well, Kate got over her cold and surprised everyone, but she is very susceptible to infection and we have to be careful. She is 10 weeks old now and still not a pound over her birth weight of 6 lb 14 oz, having difficulty with swallowing food. She has attacks of going blue each day practically, and each time I wonder if she'll get over it. I can only help her by sucking out any obstruction in her throat and soothing her. I cannot believe or describe how I feel for her, although we've been through a difficult time she has brought us so much. I don't know how I'll cope without her now.

The doctors cannot give us a 100 per cent diagnosis until they perform another muscle biopsy to see development of the tissues, this leaves us in the dark of our chances of having a healthy baby, they say there could be a high risk of it happening again.

When I started this, I was not going to write all this but somehow it all came out. I've had so many difficult feelings to cope with. I feel so disappointed that I did not have a normal birth, not seeing my baby and not feeding her myself. I wonder now if I'll ever have those experiences which I know I really need. All I know now is that above it all I am glad I have had the experience of Kate and I am grateful for that, she smiles at us now and I am often overwhelmed by the pleasure she gives us.

The birth of a handicapped baby demands such courage and endurance from parents. One has to mourn the loss of the baby one expected to have and learn to accept the person who has been born. One has to try to find out information and lines of enquiry and one has to deal with sorrow, guilt and exhaustion. (See p. 132 for a list of useful support organisations.)

Two and a half years after Kate's birth Wendy adds to her account:

Looking back on the first year after Kate was born I feel I was a different person then. After the initial shock of Kate's birth and the trauma of the first few weeks we settled into a day to day existence. Looking after a baby like Kate, not knowing what the future would hold for her made life a constant worry.

I didn't have much contact with friends at first, we lived in a very isolated place and I didn't really want to talk much on the telephone, as I had to go through everything again and again, each time I would end up in tears. It was only because of the kind persistence of a friend that I eventually got out to meet friends again. Most of my friends had babies the same age as Kate so this was very hard to cope with, just seeing how healthy they were and the progress they made through the weeks. I used to cry after friends had visited, I didn't know if it was a good thing for them to come again. But I kept on seeing them because I knew I had to go through this experience and gradually come to terms with it. Otherwise I would not have been able to cope with ordinary life which has to go on.

Mike and I had to move when Kate was only a few months old. At the time she was being tube fed and in a way I wanted the isolation of our home, but it was probably the best thing for us as I would have to really face up to reality. Now I was able to walk to shops and friends' homes so of course more people saw Kate. It was very hard for me when people naturally stop to look in a pram and then see a baby with a tube in her nose lying there looking very frail. I hadn't realised just how vulnerable and sensitive I was. I was very protective with Kate, I think I was protecting myself with this feeling, if that makes any sense. I don't know how my life would have been if Mike had not put up with me. All the difficulties I had with Kate during the day I would take out on him. I could be so bad tempered and awful, I knew what I was doing but could not stop, he always used to take it. Mike and I are very close, we were able to bear the strain no matter how hard Kate's life was or how hard ours had become, because we both loved her so much we were never going to give up on her.

I had not realised how much fear I had about our new baby until he was being born. Through pregnancy I seemed to be able to cope with the fact that this baby could have the same disease as Kate. Probably because I didn't want to believe the fact could be reality, I didn't know. Perhaps I felt like most women that it couldn't happen to them, knowing that this is not true.

When Jack was being born I cried, all the fear welled up in me and I couldn't bear to see him being born. I didn't want to be hurt and I was very frightened. My thoughts at the time went to Kate, why couldn't this have been for her, why did she have to suffer, it wasn't fair. I first saw Jack lying on the mobile unit (I don't know its name),* the doctor was checking him and he was wriggling around. I thought is he really mine? I was glad Mike had watched him being born because I somehow felt I had left him at that moment.

In the first couple of weeks after the birth I couldn't stop thinking how difficult life was for Kate and I compared the two of them and ended up in tears. Kate was over 2 years old and we had been getting along fine living a fairly normal life. Jack brought me back to the hard reality and it really hurt.

I knew that in everything Jack would do I would think of Kate, it was inevitable, there was no point trying to hide it away and pretend things were just fine, I just had to come to terms with it and live with it. Gradually life came back into perspective again and Mike and I could wonder at our new baby. It was all such a new experience I was amazed by this baby and it was wonderful to have this feeling. Mike and I were so glad we had decided to take the risk. It has strengthened our determination and love and we are very proud parents of both our lovely children.

Sheila's baby, Sam, was born when she was twenty-seven weeks pregnant. He lived for six days.

Earlier that week I had had such a strange feeling: that if I could get through the next few weeks, babe and I would be alright. I had no reason to feel this, my pregnancy was progressing normally.

It had been an active day. Paula, my pregnant friend, due nearly two months earlier than me, had been with me. We had been to our exercise class, visited neighbours

---

* Rescusitaire

and friends and been shopping. She left me late after-noon, and we arranged to go swimming that evening. I dozed, vaguely noting that I was going to the loo lots and did not feel brilliant. During the day I had had odd cramp-like pains, but had taken no notice, laughing with Paula and comparing baby movements.

I did not go swimming. I had a slight red discharge, just as I was about to leave and thought it wise to rest. It was impossible – I ached and seemed to be having irregular cramping. A bath would be soothing and help me relax sufficiently for the sensations to cease. It was not to be and I was very soon having strong pains every two to three minutes. There was a red, viscous discharge when I went to the toilet and occasionally I involuntarily bore down. I did an internal – no babe, good.[1] By now I was desperate for John to get home from swimming.

I was finding it virtually impossible to move. All my energy was completely taken up with the contractions, though I was more concerned by the blood loss, thinking I was having a placental abruption.[2]

When John arrived we rushed to hospital by ambu-lance. Whilst travelling there I began to wonder if they would have sufficient ventilators and special care equip-ment for a twenty-seven-weeker? It was only a small unit. I knew I would either have a Caesarean section or if sufficiently far on in labour, deliver my baby vaginally.

Sam was born vaginally, two hours after I realised I was in labour, very soon after I arrived at the hospital. Staff were unaware of his position and used a portable scanner to determine that he was a cephalic presentation.[3]

[1]   It is not advisable to give yourself an internal examination in labour. Sheila felt confident to do so only because she is a midwife.
[2]   When the placenta peels away from the wall of the womb before the baby is born. This is very dangerous because it stops the baby's oxygen supply and causes severe bleeding in the mother.
[3]   The baby lying head down in the womb.

I knew. If I could have got the words out I could have told them. It was not until I was asked when I had last felt any movements (about half an hour ago) that it occurred to me he might be dead. To avoid trauma to the soft tissues of his head I had an episiotomy. And suddenly he was there. He was so still and blue. 'Come on Sam,' we urged. He was badly asphyxiated and bruised. The cord was quickly cut and he was rushed to special care where he was incubated and received specialised care. John went with him.

The six days we had with Sam were so special and precious. It was like a different world, where time itself stood still. An incredibly intense period. Sam was all that mattered. That my legs became oedamatous,[4] that I had developed haemorrhoids and my blood pressure rose, were irrelevant – I had a life time to recover. Who was to know how long Sam might have? How could I possibly rest, as the midwives requested?

John and I stayed with Sam practically all the time. We talked to him and stroked his tiny limbs, head and body. His skin was so soft, warm and alive. Often he would respond and move his limbs, or clutch a finger with his hand. Bright inquisitive eyes would look round when uncovered. We played the taped music to him that I had listened to when pregnant – a soothing restful sound to detract from the constant low hum of the machinery. Sam's routine care was done by us. Just to sit by him was enough. Sometimes it seemed that wishing him to improve was enough, as we watched him, through the machines he was always connected to, fight to overcome his problems.

All our time, effort and energy were spent on Sam. In some way we were elevated and on a different plane, a level at which Sam was actually able to communicate to

4 Swelling caused by fluid retention.

us both, separately. There were times when we did feel negative, but generally we felt strong and positive and were able to encourage each other to always be strong for Sam. We constantly gave him as much love, energy and support as we were able to and while we desperately wanted him to live, we understood that it was for our own more selfish reasons and what was really important was that we supported Sam in whatever it was he needed to do, even if that meant dying.

We love him deeply and always will. He gave us so much that we have to be grateful for. He has brought us even closer together, given us a far greater awareness and insight into life and enriched our lives in so many ways. I feel proud and honoured that he chose us to help him live his short life.

In the hospital staff were generally wonderful. Minor irritations were amateurish attempts at counselling, lack of communication between wards, lack of gowns to fit and photograph Sam in and only an enormous coffin to see him in, in the chapel of rest (since rectified – there is now a lovely little crib). There was no help with funeral arrangements – we made our own.

Once home, close friends gave support. Often I needed to withdraw and be alone. We had some lovely letters. People who had had similar experiences invariably responded well. Acquaintances rarely knew what to say – if I felt strong I helped them, but if not I would feel frustrated. The worst thing is to be ignored. Basically it does not matter what anyone says as long as they acknowledge the death in some way.

Sheila pointed out that if your baby dies, nobody will let you be post-natal because you embarrass them. We must learn to say to our friends, our neighbours, our sisters who have this terrible experience, 'I'm sorry your baby died.' We must learn to hear and respond to and weep with our friends who suffer such losses, and not to pretend it does not happen, or shut them out of groups, or classes, or other activities, or social contact, because we are embarrassed by the enormity of their loss, or the rude health of our own children. After a stillbirth or an early death of a baby, the mother's body pours with blood and milk just as after any other birth and it seems like a fountain of grief that will just go on and on.

It may help to call SANDS, the Stillbirth and Neonatal Death Society (see p. 133), if you feel it would be useful to talk to other parents who have been through the same experience. If you cannot contact or find any appropriate helpline and feel in despair, you can always contact the Samaritans if you can get to a telephone. Their number is in all local telephone directories.

Sheila became pregnant again shortly after Sam's death. Halfway through her second pregnancy, she said:

> I am twenty-four weeks pregnant now. After Sam died all my rationality and reason said wait, recover physically and mentally, but every ounce of my being wanted to be pregnant. I felt it would not have happened if it had not been right. Initially John and I did not talk about this pregnancy and pushed it to the back of our minds not daring to think about it or wanting to be hurt again. I did not confirm the pregnancy until I was thirteen weeks or tell people until I was twenty weeks.
>
> Now I feel so overwhelmed by the intensity of emotion I feel when I think about this pregnancy. I am so confident that everything will be just perfect this time. I am so ecstatically happy and it is only possible thanks to Sam.

However, our hearts must go out to Sheila and John, because shortly afterwards their second baby, Cara, was born dead.

In the autumn of 1987 Liz and Dave had a baby girl called Emily. Liz has written about Emily's brief life, sharing her feelings in the belief that it may help anyone else who goes through an experience like this to feel less alone, and also help anyone who hasn't been through anything like this to have some insight into what it is like.

27 September. Emily was now fourteen days overdue, and my original fear for the forthcoming labour had become impatient anticipation! Dave and I had just celebrated my twenty-ninth birthday with a very large meal at our next door neighbour's house. On returning home at 11 p.m. regular contractions commenced – coming every five minutes but not painful.

1 a.m. Phoned labour ward. Pains now every two minutes but still not particularly painful. I was assured by the midwife that I probably was in labour, but to wait at home until contractions were more painful. Continued to clear up kitchen and make preparations for damson jam.

1.30 a.m. Had a bath. Bowels opened four times in an hour.

2 a.m. Dave got up and I told him about contractions. Back to bed where Dave started to massage my back while I leant on the bean bag.

2.30 a.m. Started to feel sick and regretted eating such a big meal. Worried that this might be transition so we decided to go to the hospital. Keith came round to look after Tom. By this time contractions quite painful – having to lean on the table and breathe through them.

3 a.m. Arrived at labour ward. I was soon settled on the bed with a bean bag. I was relieved to hear that they weren't busy tonight (last time was pretty hectic). An

internal examination revealed I was 4 cm dilated. This caused mixed feelings – relief that I wasn't just suffering the effects of a tummy bug (I had wondered) – disappointed that I suspected hours of pain were ahead.

The midwife broke my waters to find lots of meconium. This had happened with Thomas and we knew that doctors from special care would be present at the birth but otherwise there was no panic. As before a monitor was placed on baby's head (but I was still able to kneel up on the bean bag for the rest of the first stage).

3.15 a.m. Vomited that huge meal and felt better for it!

3.30 a.m. Painful! Started to use gas and air every three contractions (so that I had something to look forward to!). I was enjoying the experience of being quite *compos mentis* in between contractions – with Thomas I'd had pethidine and about three hours had passed with no communication between myself and Dave. This time I could ask him to vary the massage or just ask his opinion. During contractions I leant on the bean bag and rocked my hips quite violently from side to side. Dave tried valiantly to hold on to me and massage where possible.

4 a.m. Little time seemed to have passed since I was '4 cm' and yet the pain seemed awful. I feared many hours of labour yet and began to doubt that I'd make it. Asked the midwife for pethidine. After some discussion she persuaded me to use just gas and air but with every contraction. She said I had about two hours to go but to my relief she didn't do a vaginal examination (I didn't want to know that I might have progressed only 1 cm!).

4–5.30 a.m. My memory of this is a little foggy. Contractions seemed to follow relentlessly with little time in between to recover. I was conscious of groaning and moaning on outbreaths – to make myself breathe out –

but I didn't feel inhibited this time. Eventually groans became sobs and I began to feel it was all too much. I remember crying out 'I want my mummy' and being transported back in my mind to very frightening moments in my childhood. The midwife came in to see what all the noise was about and asked if I wanted to push. 'I don't know,' I wailed. A few minutes later I was beginning to push and I could hear the rustle of preparations by the midwife.

5.30 a.m. The midwife agreed to my pushing in a kneeling position (propped on bean bags). The first few pushes were a great improvement on my previous labour experience. I could almost feel Emily moving down. It was such a relief because I'd toiled for two hours trying to push Thomas out. I was sure this improvement was due to kneeling rather than being on my back.

After a while I was asked to turn round because the midwives couldn't reach Emily well enough. I sat on the bed and pushed again. I became aware of the special care staff waiting by the bed. Dave could see they were having some problems trying to get their fingers on Emily so he said very sternly 'Do *exactly* as they say.' Emily's head came out and I panted while they sucked her out.

5.55 a.m. Another push and she slithered out – just like the books say. I said happily 'She's a girl!' – the midwife was preventing Emily from breathing[1] and the doctor was sucking her tubes out. I wasn't elated but I was quite pleased with myself as things had been much better than I'd expected.

After some more sucking out Emily was taken to special care and I was already starting to worry because

[1]   This may be necessary to try to prevent the baby from inhaling meconium.

she didn't seem to be responding well – she was going blue and was very floppy. The doctor said she was having difficulty breathing. All the nurses said 'Don't worry – she's in good hands.'

Nine hours later Emily died. She had inhaled too much thick meconium for her lungs to work. The staff on special care of course did all they could and were extremely supportive but little Emily was only ours for a short time. We miss her so much.

If you face the tragedy of stillbirth or the challenge of caring for a baby born with a handicap, try to find some space in yourself to remember that you matter too, that you need to take care of yourself. For some people taking care of themselves will mean making demands on other people. On the other hand one may want space and privacy, or move between these two states.

You might find it useful to read more about the subject or to share your experience with trusted friends. If you don't want to share with friends, consider going to your GP and asking to be put in touch with a professional counsellor. A few hospitals have a midwife specially trained as a 'grief counsellor', and if so she will be made available to you, but it is all too rare. The exercises in this book, taken gently, and done alone if you feel too fragile to work with other people, may help to clarify things a little.

Those of us with healthy babies should remember not to ignore or avoid our friends whose babies have difficulties, and anyone setting up groups or classes should also be careful not to exclude women in these situations: 'The worst thing of all is to be ignored.'

CHAPTER 7

Closing the Circle – ending these explorations, beginning others

This is the last, exploratory, chapter of the book. It is time to collect together all the work you have done, and to look towards the future. If you are in a group it is time to take a look at everything you have been through together, and to close your circle. Although this can feel sad, it marks the beginning of a new phase. Use it as a time to collect your thoughts, balance yourself, and make any decisions you feel ready to about moving on.

Exercise 50   Reviewing the sessions

Cast your mind over the work you have done over the last few weeks. It may be a surprise to realise just how much material you have covered. If you are working alone by making a notebook, read back through it, and recall all the questions and issues you have addressed yourself to. In a group have a quick brainstorm together and recall all the ground you have covered. If you have followed this book in sequence you will have thought about the special quality of yourself; of your self as a mother, and your own mother; you will have thought all about your body and your relationship with it; you will have considered assertiveness;

and you will have explored your desire for more children or your decision not to have more children. Remind yourself of how you opened up these questions together.

Exercise 51   Reviewing the experience

Write a list for yourself: the most surprising thing I've discovered; the most shocking thing I've come across; the saddest thing I've come across; the most exciting thing I discovered; the most encouraging thing I've found out; the happiest thing I've found out or discovered; I've thought more about . . . I've understood . . .

Have a good ten minutes to write about all those things in terms of what you've come across in your sessions with the different chapters. Read and absorb these features of your experience. If you are in a group, in turn, share what you have written with everyone else, and talk around each point a little. It is lovely to hear how different points and different moments have been important to different people.

Exercise 52   What happens next?

If you often attend groups, or have long heart-to-heart talks with friends, or make lengthy reviews of your life by yourself, you will be familiar with the predicament of feeling an immediate 'high' after the contact or the new resolution you have made which is followed, after ten days or ten hours or even ten minutes, by an anti-climax and sense that you are bogged down and nothing can change.

Try to avoid that unrealistic high and unpleasant low by making some realistic and pragmatic plans. Cast your mind over all the work and thinking you have done in the past weeks. Are there any decisions that you feel ready to make – however small, however large. If so, make a note of them in your book, plus any practical things you need to find out to follow up your decision. If you are in a group, share your decisions with the other women.

The spectacular nature of these decisions was often striking: I was amazed how many women applied for, and got, new jobs, or places at college and on training courses, while they were coming to the post-natal group, and how other women resolved inner conflicts and outer pressures deciding to stay at home with their babies for the first, say, ten, twelve or twenty-four months, with a commitment to review the situation again after that.

Many women make decisions regarding their health, strength and fitness – making time for dance, judo, karate, running, or altering habits of diet or alcohol or nicotine consumption, or making adequate sleep and rest a priority. Many women had felt their attention drawn to their need for self-nourishment. Commitments were made towards making space, time, money, for small or large pleasant times for ourselves; to have saunas, massages, time to swim without the baby; a walk alone or a baby-free wander round the shops; a pleasant evening with a friend at least once a fortnight, or a lie in bed with cups of tea and books or magazines to read in the early evening or late morning; to buy aromatics of all kinds – bath cubes, bubbles, soothing colognes, and fragrant oils.

Decisions also arose in the area of assertiveness. Assertive responses were practised and eventually put into action – in the reviewing and re-evaluating of partnerships; reorganising and sharing responsibility for baby care and house care; making progress in relationships with other family members and professionals, like doctors and health visitors, who had sometimes been experienced as overwhelming.

Lots of women made a decision to have more fun – to make space for the lighter side of life, to avoid feeling swamped by the sheer complexity and heaviness of life.

You can do this in many ways. Wearing bright colours, taking every chance to dance or sing, alone and in company, sticking cartoons that make you laugh on the wall, and taking every opportunity that arises to laugh with friends about the ludicrous aspects of life with a new baby.

Women describing their labours often mention moments of high comedy as well as drama and seriousness and, in the same way, just a chance to go over the mad happenings of your day with a friend may bring the welcome release of laughter – even if it is mildly hysterical.

On your list of plans, only write things that you can achieve or get to grips with in the near future, then enjoy the satisfaction of carrying your plans out. There are no magic answers or magic solutions; just small, specific and attainable steps towards change.

Exercise 53   Affirmations

If you are working alone, get your notebook and your colours out. Make a picture or large design of your first name, the name people choose to call you by. Use shapes, colours, and decorations around the letters of your name that celebrate the kind of person you are.

Now write around your name all your positive qualities. Are you:

gentle	loud	creative	positive
sensitive	sensible	fit	supple
imaginative	perceptive	clever	intelligent
musical	sensual	generous	dynamic
peaceful	articulate	logical	brave
honest	open	caring	magnificent?

Write any or all of those on your design, and anything else positive that you know you are. Write the words in appropriate colours and styles.

Throwing compliments game

Are you especially good at anything, however 'unimportant'? Write it on. This is no time for modesty. Enjoy affirming your positive qualities. See if you find it easier than you did six weeks ago, or whenever you began working with this book: 'I'm very good at . . .'

> dancing
> driving
> my job
> singing
> collage
> calming down crises
> making people feel important
> making brave decisions
> keeping in touch with friends
> speaking my mind
> giving parties
> making jam
> making lists

You should also affirm someone else. This is a vital way for women to empower one another, and to begin to break down the conditioning which inclines women to feel competitive with one another. If there is something you admire in a woman in your life, tell her, pay her a compliment, be open about it. It will not take anything away from you, and on the contrary, will make you feel stronger too. Say as specifically as you can what you admire, appreciate, feel excited by, enjoy, or celebrate, in her.

If you are working in a group, have a good five minutes to think clearly about each other woman in your group, and the compliment you would most like to pay her. Write your compliments down – because in the emotion of the moment you may forget them otherwise. Then find some pleasant object you can pass around. We used a pair of legwarmers rolled up into a ball – but anything pleasing to look at and hold will do.

One person should begin by holding the object. She should choose the person she wants to give a compliment to, make eye contact with her, and say her compliment clearly, giving the object to the woman receiving the compliment. The woman receiving the compliment should try not to disclaim it in any way or protest about it, but pause for a moment to take it in properly. She then gives someone else a compliment and passes the object on to them. Proceeding in a random order, everyone will eventually have given a compliment to everyone else. Passing an object around helps to make the giving and receiving action clear, and helps one not to rush.

Oddly enough, this is an incredibly difficult exercise to do. It makes everyone feel shaky and vulnerable, but also delighted. Giving clear affirmations, and receiving them, without protesting or disclaiming, is an art we could all try to learn:

'Balbinder, I love your deep clear voice.'
'Terry, I admire your work in hospitals. It needs doing
    and you do it so well.'
'Sharon, I enjoy your easy elegance.'
'Juliet, your sense of humour is marvellous.'
'Colleen, I feel you are a very understanding and warm
    person.'
'Kim, I think you have endured a lot and are very brave.'

Exercise 54   Closing the circle

If you have worked through the exercises in this book alone
you could choose this moment to pause for a time in your
active explorations. You could now leave a few months for
the thoughts and ideas that have arisen to settle, and for
you to settle and absorb what has gone on. We are strangely
bereft of rituals in our modern chaotic urban life. It might
be useful to have a small ritual to mark the end of your
work: I don't mean anything spooky or heavy – eat a lovely
cake, or light a candle, or have a walk in the sun, or
anything you enjoy. While you are doing it, have in mind
that you are, for the time being, letting go of this kind of
work, and when you finish, say to yourself – OK – I let it go.

If you are in a group, all join hands, or place your hands
on each other's shoulders, or link up physically somehow.
Let someone read out this final meditation:

Feel yourself sitting firmly based on the ground. Sit up
tall, out of your hips. Breathe a little more deeply and a
little more slowly than usual, hear the breath coming and
going in your throat. Let your eyes close. Become aware
of yourself as part of this group. Let your mind travel
over all the work and all the caring and sharing that you
have done in previous weeks . . . (Pause) . . . Now allow
yourself to feel that when, in the future, you work on,

and struggle with, and laugh about, and cry about, the work of being a woman with a young baby, you take with you the love and support of everybody else in this group . . . so be aware of yourself as part of the group . . . when you feel like it gradually release your contact and blink your eyes open.

Now your group work is over. Of course it's sad – the end of anything is sad, but even that we can learn from. Friendships may have formed, and you may continue to meet some of the other people, without the particular electricity and purpose of the group, but perhaps with a continuing and sustaining enjoyment.

Leave three months or so before you work your way through this whole cycle of exercises again. You may of course want to dip into the book, do odd things, remind yourself of particular exercises; but it would cause too much upheaval to go through the whole lot again without a proper break. In three months time your baby will be quite different, you will be quite different, and you may well find it worthwhile to examine all those issues all over again.

The work we have done is really the work of people trying to do mothering in a fragmented and often unhappy society. As the guardians and nourishers of future generations we are rarely honoured, respected, supported, or cared for. Most of the time we are invisible, broke, rejected, and pushed out. Although the work we do is the most important work anybody could do, society as a whole does not realise this and does not care. Our society does not wish to take care of us and our fellow-mothers in our creative urgent work. So, for the time being, we must take care of each other, and we must take care of ourselves.

Useful Organisations and Addresses

Yoga

The British Wheel of Yoga, 445 High Road, Ilford, Essex IG1 1TR

Iyengar Teachers Association, 8 Vale Road, London N4 1PZ

Post-Natal Support

National Childbirth Trust, 9 Queensborough Terrace, London W2

Caesarean Support Group, 42 Shelford Road, Trumpington, Cambridge

National Housewives Register, Antoinette Ferraro, 245 Warwick Road, Solihull, W. Midlands

Support for Handicapped Children and their Parents

Association for Spina Bifida and Hydrocephalus, Tavistock House North, Tavistock Square, London WC1 9HJ

Down's Children Association, 4 Oxford Street, London W1N 9FL

MENCAP, 123 Golden Lane, London ECY 0RT
Spastics Society, 12 Park Crescent, London W1N 4EQ
'Does He Take Sugar' and 'In Touch' – during series on
Radio 4, helpline on day of programme 01-480-4411

Support if a Baby Dies

Stillbirth and Neo-Natal Death Society, 37 Christchurch
Hill, London NW3 1LA

24-Hour Crisis Line

Samaritans – in all local telephone directories

Further Reading

Yoga and Exercise

Fonda, Jane (1987), *Jane Fonda's New Workout and Weight Loss Programme*, Viking

Polden, Margie and Whiteford, Barbara (1984), *Post Natal Exercise*, Century

Carefully explained and graded exercises from day one after delivery to full fitness

Widdowson, Ros (1982), *Yoga Made Easy*, Hamlyn

Tobias, Maxine, and Stewart, Mary (1985), *Stretch and Relax*, Dorling Kindersley

A full, clear, and excellent book of yoga exercises, including ante- and post-natal sections

Fertility

Davidson, John and Farida (1986), *Natural Fertility Awareness*, Daniel

Assertiveness

Dickson, Ann (1982), *A Woman in Your Own Right*, Quartet
A comprehensive guide to the methods of personal assertiveness

Psychology

Baker Miller, Jean (1978), *Towards a New Psychology of Women*, Penguin
Disentangles the sexism in pre-feminist psychological theory, and lives up to its promising title
Ernst, Sheila, and Goddison, Lucy (1981), *In Our Own Hands*, Women's Press
An indispensable book of self-help exploratory exercises for women and groups trying to find their way
Ernst, Sheila, and Maguire, Marie (1987), *Living With the Sphinx*, Women's Press
Papers from the Women's Therapy Centre help us all to understand the struggle for perception, growth, and personal revolution
French, Marilyn (1986), *Beyond Power – Women, Men, and Morals*, Abacus
Huge, fascinating book examines women's place in history all over the world, pleads for the chance, through female energy, of the planet's survival

Assaults and Self-Defence

Brownmiller, Susan (1975), *Against Our Will*, Pelican
Susan Brownmiller gives us the dreadful history of rape and urges us to deny it a future
Quinn, Kaleghl (1983), *Stand Your Ground*, Orbis
Physical, mental and spiritual exercises for self-defence

Novels

Oakley, Ann (1984), *Taking It Like a Woman*, Flamingo
Being a woman, being a mother, over the last three decades
Armstrong, Penny, and Feldman, Sheryl (1986), *The Gentle Art*, Corgi
Loving midwifery among the Amish community in America

Alther, Lisa (1985), *Other Women*, Penguin
One woman's journey through the discoveries of therapy

Death

Kubler Ross, Elizabeth (1982), *Death and Dying*, Souvenir Press
Talking with terminally ill patients, the author gives us a chance
   to begin to think clearly and creatively about death

Index

CHANGING LIVES

Our selection of Handbooks designed to represent the changing
lives of women today is growing fast.

BIRTH AND OUR BODIES

by Paddy O'Brien

This practical and positive companion guide provides women
with detailed physical and mental exercises to practice through
pregnancy and birth.

Working chronologically from the time when a woman may
not even be pregnant but hopes to conceive in the near future,
right through to the birth itself, the guide provides a
comprehensive exercise programme for relaxation, combating
morning sickness, stage fright in the last few weeks of pregnancy
and for strengthening the pelvic floor muscles.
0-86358-047-5   144pp

YOUR BODY, YOUR BABY, YOUR LIFE

by Angela Phillips
with Nicky Leap and Barbara Jacobs

Written by the co-editor of the British edition of OUR BODIES,
OURSELVES, a non-patronising, non-moralising, non-sexist
guide to pregnancy and childbirth.
0-86358-006-8   222pp   illustrated with diagrams and
cartoons

RUNNING
The Women's Handbook

by Liz Sloan and Ann Kramer
With illustrations by Jo Nesbitt and Elaine Anderson

A handbook for the hundreds and thousands of women who run
or want to start running – enabling women to lead a fitter freer
life.
0-86358-043-2   138pp   illustrated

CHANGES OF HEART
Reflections on the Theme of Women's Independence

by Liz Heron

Using an original format of combining beautiful and incisive prose, interviews with women, and personal pieces about the author's own life, *Changes of Heart* is an unusual, uplifting and thought-provoking foray into the lives of women today.

With strong contextual pieces on the politics and culture which surround and form our consciousnesses, Liz Heron explores how women's lives have been altered by the social changes of the last two decades, and how women's relationships with men and with women have been touched or altered by these changes.

0-86358-028-9p   224pp

A WEALTH OF EXPERIENCE
The Lives of Older Women

Edited by Susan Hemmings

It is often hard for people to think of growing older in a positive way, but this book shows the strength and dignity of eighteen women who are now aged between 40 and 65.

These women talk openly about their lives, about the political changes and growth in women's consciousness that they have witnessed and experienced through the twentieth century. *A Wealth of Experience* is a celebration of the achievements of older women, of their ability to survive hardships which are familiar to all women. This book is a patchwork of personal histories and political ideas that reflect some of the best characteristics of oral history such as the release of knowledge and experience of people normally silenced. But it is also an invaluable guide for all women; for older women to identify some common roots and shared causes and for younger women who will one day join their number.

0-86358-031-9p   192pp

FIT FOR THE FUTURE
The Guide for Women who Want to Live Well

by Jeanette Winterson

A complete manual for any woman who wants to live well, providing a philosophy of fitness which is compulsive – covers exercise, diet, sex, sports . . .
0-86358-072-6p   144pp   illustrated
0-86358-053-Xh

THE PATIENT PATIENTS
Women and Their Doctors

by Helen Roberts

What do doctors think about their patients? And what do women think of their doctors? Helen Roberts investigates the relationship between women and their doctors and sets out to answer such questions as the reasons for women's ill health and the support, or lack of it, they get from their families.

She suggests changes that will benefit both patients and doctors and provides a sensitive portrayal of women, *The Patient Patients*

'Nearly every woman will see in these pages a reflection of herself in her relationship with doctors.'

Sheila Kitzinger

0-86358-019-Xp   130pp

DISCOVERING WOMEN'S HISTORY
A Practical Manual

by Deirdre Beddoe

'An invaluable and fascinating guide to the raw material for anyone approaching this unexplored territory.'
The Sunday Times

0-86358-008-4   232pp   illustrated

ON YOUR OWN
A Guide for Independent Women

by Jean Shapiro

A bible for all divorced and widowed women, covering all of the practical and emotional matters that women are likely to face when they find themselves suddenly 'on their own'.
0-86358-027-0h   250pp   illustrated
0-86358-045-9p

NATURAL HEALING IN GYNECOLOGY
A User's Guide

by Rina Nissim

'. . . compels us to care for our health in an intelligent and truly preventive manner. It provides a range of healing alternatives from Eastern and Western cultures, and critiques the limits of conventional Western medicine, giving us the power of choice . . . An unusual and valuable resource indeed.'
Boston Women's Health Book Collective
0-86358-063-7h   192pp   illustrated
0-86358-069-6p

Also Available from Pandora Press

Test Tube Women: What Future for Motherhood?		
Rita Arditti and Renate Duelli Klein (eds)	£4.95	☐
The Midwife Challenge *Sheila Kitzinger* (ed.)	£6.95	☐
Natural Healing in Gynecology *Rina Nissim*	£4.95	☐
Birth and Our Bodies *Paddy O'Brien*	£4.95	☐
Your Life After Birth *Paddy O'Brien*	£4.95	☐
Women's Health: *A Spare Rib* Reader		
Sue O'Sullivan (ed.)	£5.95	☐
The Politics of Breastfeeding *Gabrielle Palmer*	£6.95	☐
Motherhood: What It Does To Your Mind *Jane Price*	£4.95	☐
Women and the AIDS Crisis *Diane Richardson*	£3.95	☐
The Patient Patients: Women and Their Doctors		
Helen Roberts	£3.95	☐
The Tentative Pregnancy: Prenatal Diagnosis and the		
Future of Motherhood *Barbara Katz Rothman*	£5.95	☐
A Child: Your Choice *Jean Shapiro*	£4.95	☐
On Your Own: A Guide to Independent Living		
Jean Shapiro	£6.95	☐
Running: The Women's Handbook *Liz Sloan and Ann Kramer*	£4.50	☐
The Heroin Users *Tam Stewart*	£5.95	☐
Fit For the Future *Jeanette Winterson*	£3.95	☐

All these books are available at your local bookshop or can be ordered direct by post. Just tick the titles you want and fill in the form below.

Name ....

Address ....

....

....

Write to Unwin Hyman Cash Sales, PO Box 11, Falmouth, Cornwall TR10 9EN.

Please enclose remittance to the value of the cover price plus:

UK: 60p for the first book plus 25p for the second book, thereafter 15p for each additional book ordered to a maximum charge of £1.90.

BFPO and EIRE: 60p for the first book plus 25p for the second book and 15p per copy for the next 7 books and thereafter 9p per book.

OVERSEAS INCLUDING EIRE: £1.25 for the first book plus 75p for the second book and 28p for each additional book.

Pandora Press reserve the right to show new retail prices on covers which may differ from those previously advertised in the text or elsewhere. Postage rates are also subject to revision.